KAKURO PUZZLES

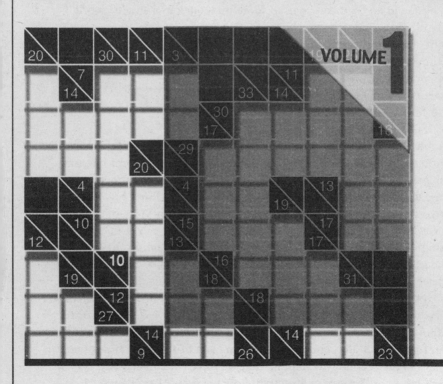

VOLUME 1

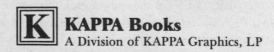

KAPPA Books
A Division of KAPPA Graphics, LP

INTRODUCTION

Welcome to the world of Kakuro! Like its similarly Japanese-named cousin Sudoku, the Kakuro puzzle is actually of American origin; Kappa Books has been publishing them for years as Cross Addition puzzles. Kakuro puzzles are based very closely on crossword puzzles. The reason they look different is that the "clues" are so short they fit within the puzzle diagram itself. As you can see in the puzzle fragment below, the clues are just numbers embedded in gray squares on one side or another of a diagonal line. The 24 in the top row below signifies that the three white squares directly below it are to be filled with digits that add up to 24. Likewise, the 35 in the third row means that the sum of the digits in the seven white squares to its right will be 35. The numbers that go in the blanks are the digits 1 to 9 (no zeroes!), and no digit can be used more than once in a single "word."

It might seem like a daunting task at first to deduce from this scant information the unique correct responses, but a little familarity with the puzzles and a few rules of thumb will make it all very doable.

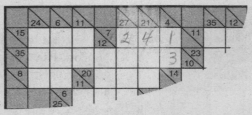

Notice that some of the smallest and largest possible sums can only be expressed one way, while ones in the middle of the range are more uncertain. That is, there's only one way to express 3 or 17 as the sum of two different numbers ("1 + 2" and "8 + 9"), and lots of ways to express 11 ("2 + 9," "3 + 8," "4 + 7," and "5 + 6"). Let's try an example in our sample diagram. Look at the 4 in the top row which indicates that the two numbers below it add up to 4. The 4 doesn't indicate "2 + 2" since a 2 can only be used once. Thus, the 4 means "1 + 3" (or "3 + 1"). One could pencil in "1,3" in each of the two blanks below the 4. Next, look at the 7 in the second row. The only three unique digits that can add up to 7 are 1, 2, and 4, in some order. Therefore, one could pencil in "1,2,4" in each of the three blanks next to the 7 in the second row. Notice that we have established two sets of possibilities for the square directly below the 4 — "1 or 3" and "1 or 2 or 4." Do you see that, since 1 is the only digit in both sets, this square can only hold a 1? We'll return to this example again in a while.

Because it's so important to recognize sums like these with unique representations, we've put together a table (shown at the top of the next page) that summarizes this information.

"WORD" LENGTH	MINIMUM SUM	MAXIMUM SUM	UNIQUE REPRESENTATIONS			
2	3	17	3=1+2	4=1+3	16=7+9	17=8+9
3	6	24	6=1+2+3	7=1+2+4	23=6+8+9	24=7+8+9
4	10	30	10=1+2+3+4	11=1+2+3+5	29=5+7+8+9	30=6+7+8+9
5	15	35	15=1+2+3+4+5	16=1+2+3+4+6	34=4+6+7+8+9	35=5+6+7+8+9
6	21	39	21=1+2+3+4+5+6	22=1+2+3+4+5+7	38=3+5+6+7+8+9	39=4+5+6+7+8+9
7	28	42	28=1+2+3+4+5+6+7	29=1+2+3+4+5+6+8	41=2+4+5+6+7+8+9	42=3+4+5+6+7+8+9
8	36	44	All sums have unique representations			
9	45	45	45=1+2+3+4+5+6+7+8+9			

Let's look at how the table is organized. Suppose you have four blanks that add up to 11, you can look at the row in the table corresponding to a word-length of 4. Reading across that row, you will first see that the sum of four digits is no less than 10 and no more than 30. Continuing along, you'll see that there are four sums with unique representations. In particular, you'll see that 11 can only be expressed as a sum of four different digits in only one way: 1 + 2 + 3 + 5.

The information in this table can also be used in slightly more subtle ways. Let's go back to our sample diagram. We determined before that there's a 1 in the square below the 4. Since we saw that the "word" next to the 7 consists of a 1, a 2, and a 4, in some order, the digit directly below the 21 is a 2 or a 4. That number, added to the two below it, gives a sum of 21. If we look in the table at the row corresponding to a word-length of 3, we won't get any help; 21 isn't a sum with a unique representation. However, we can use the table to see that the two bottom digits for our sum of 21 can add up to no more than 17. Thus, the top digit must be at least (21 - 17 =) 4. Since we already know that it's 2 or 4, we can deduce that it's a 4. We can also use the table to determine that the two numbers directly below the 4 sum to (21 - 4 =) 17, so they are 8 and 9, in some order.

Often, extreme sums aren't enough to get us all the way to a solution. In such a case, one whittles down the list of possibilities as best one can, working back and forth between the "across" clues and the "down" clues. Figuring out a digit sometimes leads to a chain of deductions that flows back halfway across the puzzle to help with a sticky problem. We've provided a scratch pad for each puzzle, so you can test out sums and eliminate impossibilities.

Be warned, the problems get more difficult as you advance through the magazine. Good luck and happy solving!

Kakuro 1

Scratch pad: 9+2, 6+5, 7+4, 8+3
4+5+9

Kakuro 2

Scratch pad:

7	5	11	12	10	13	9
6+1	4+1	7+4	6+6	4+7	8+5	5+4
5+2	3+2	6+5	7+5		9+4	3+6
4+3		3+8	4+3		7+6	2+7
		2+9	8+4			1+8

10	6
6+4	2+4
7+3	
8+2	
4+1	

Kakuro 3

Scratch pad:

Kakuro 4

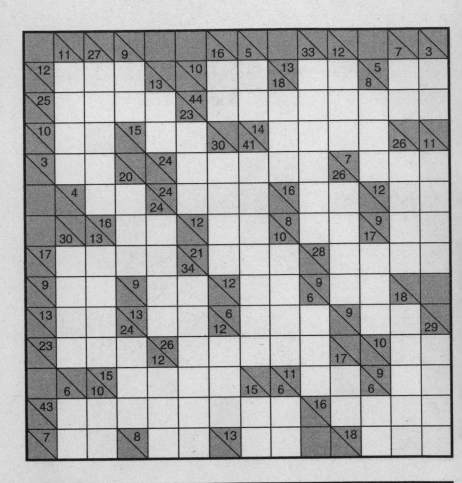

Scratch pad:

Kakuro 5

Scratch pad:

Kakuro 6

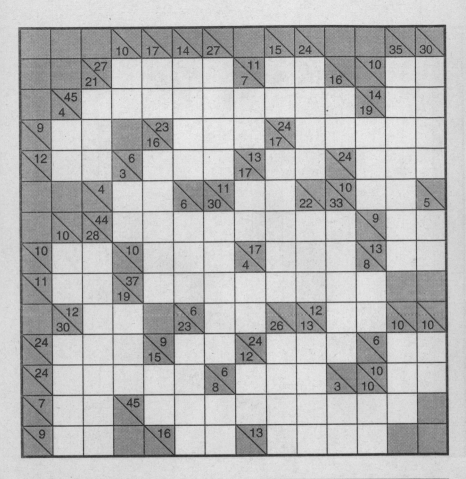

Scratch pad:

Kakuro 7

Scratch pad:

Kakuro 8

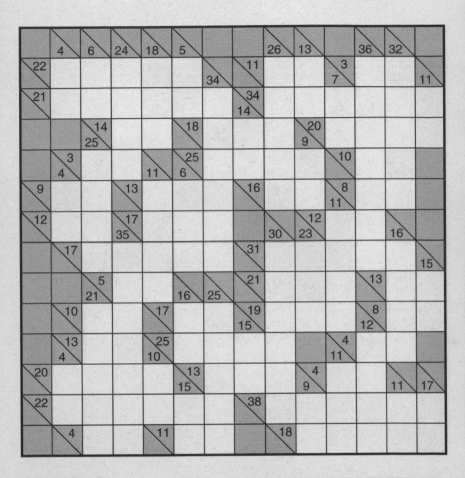

Scratch pad:

Kakuro 9

Kakuro 10

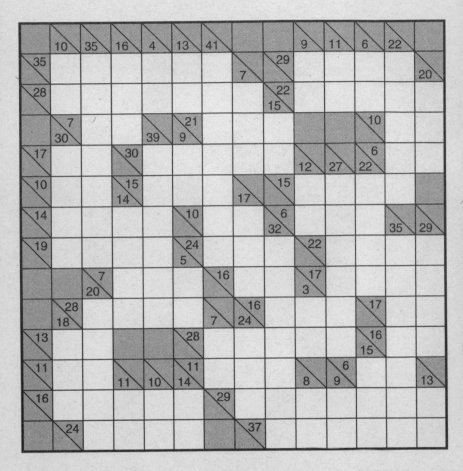

Scratch pad:

Kakuro 11

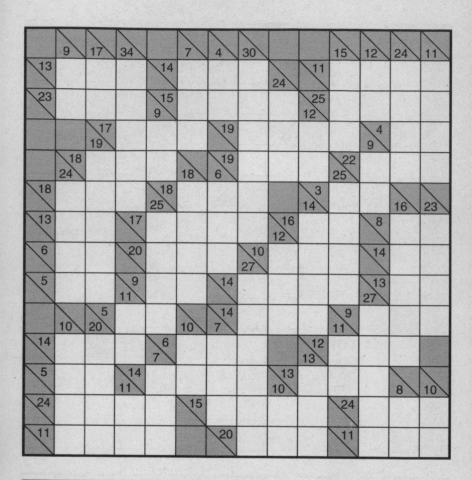

Scratch pad:

Kakuro 12

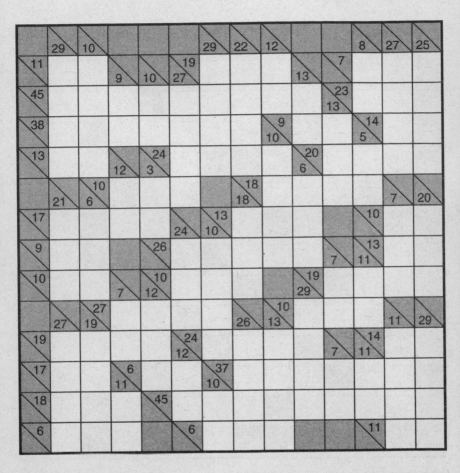

Scratch pad:

Kakuro 13

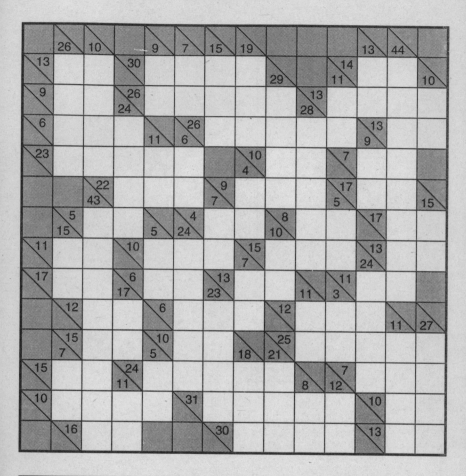

Scratch pad:

Kakuro 14

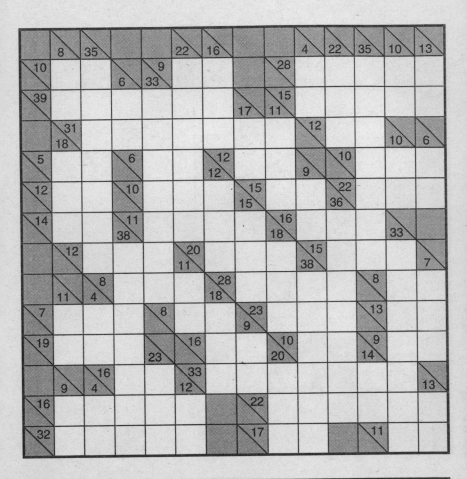

Scratch pad:

Kakuro 15

Scratch pad:

Kakuro 16

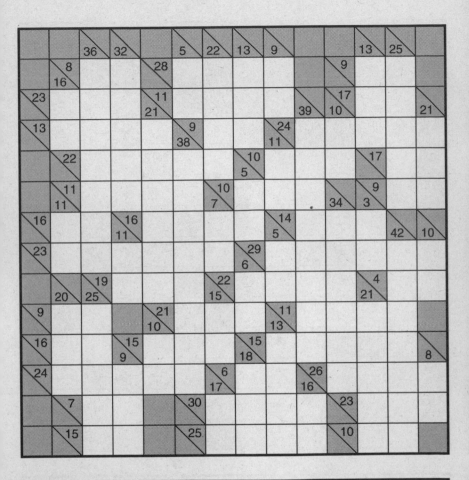

Scratch pad:

Kakuro 17

Scratch pad:

Kakuro 18

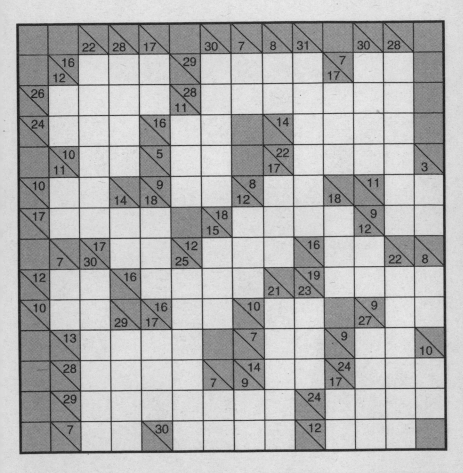

Scratch pad:

Kakuro 19

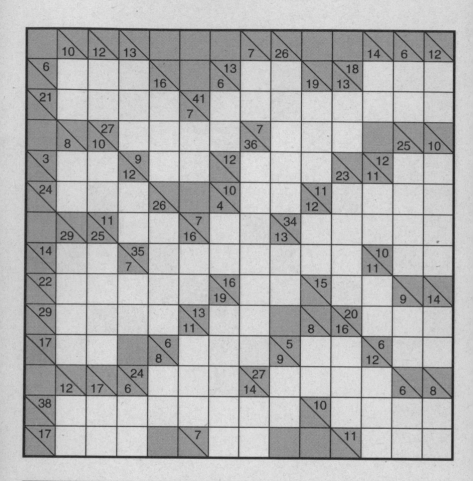

Scratch pad:

Kakuro 20

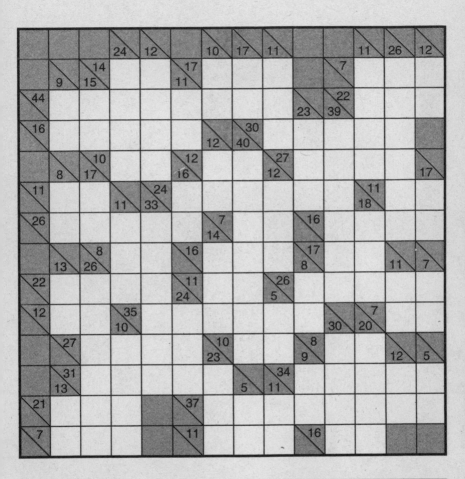

Scratch pad:

Kakuro 21

Scratch pad:

Kakuro 22

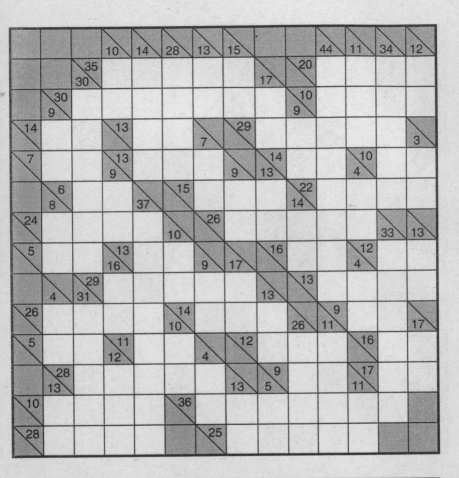

Scratch pad:

Kakuro 23

Scratch pad:

Kakuro 24

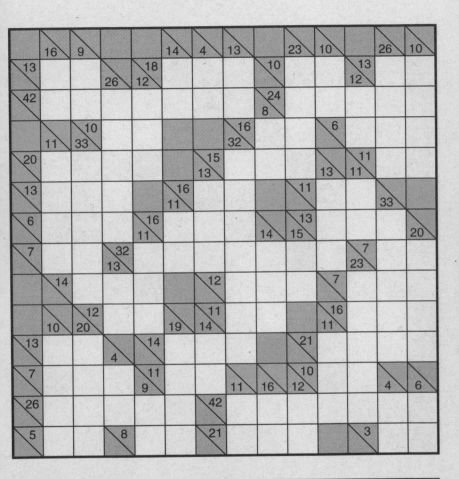

Scratch pad:

Kakuro 25

Scratch pad:

Kakuro 26

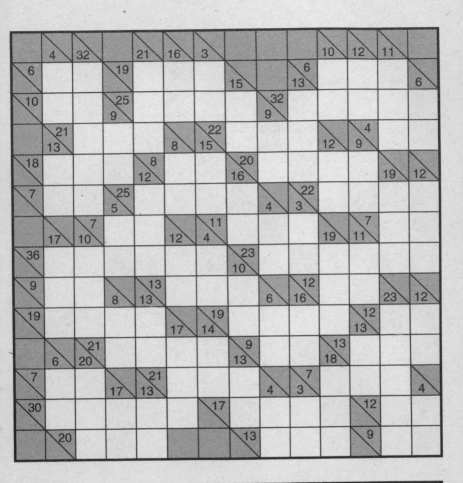

Scratch pad:

Kakuro 27

Scratch pad:

Kakuro 28

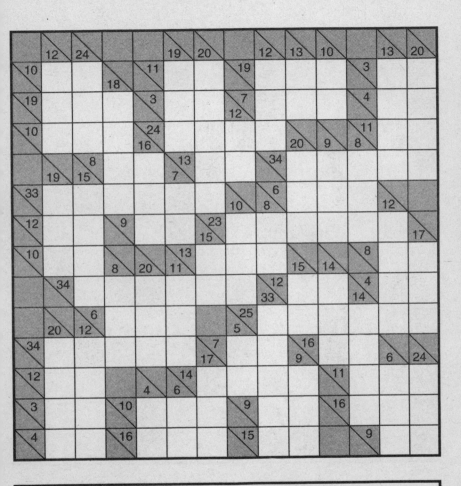

Scratch pad:

Kakuro 29

Scratch pad:

Kakuro 30

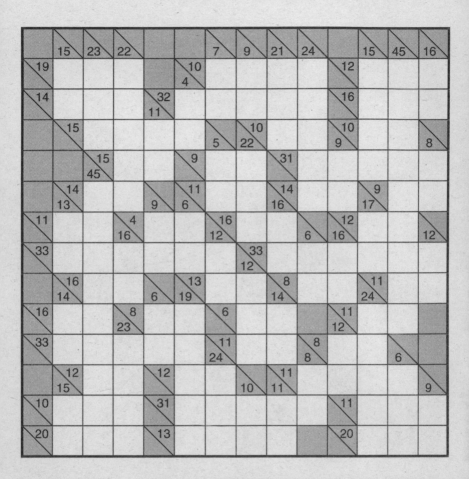

Scratch pad:

Kakuro 31

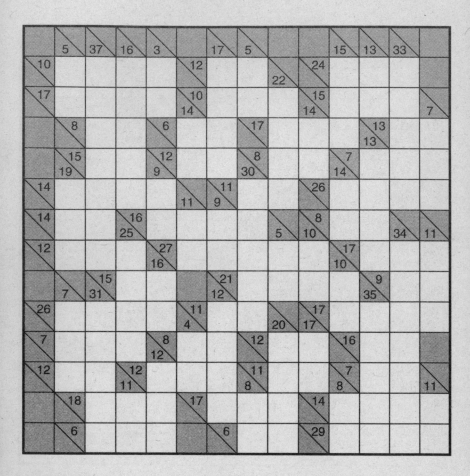

Scratch pad:

Kakuro 32

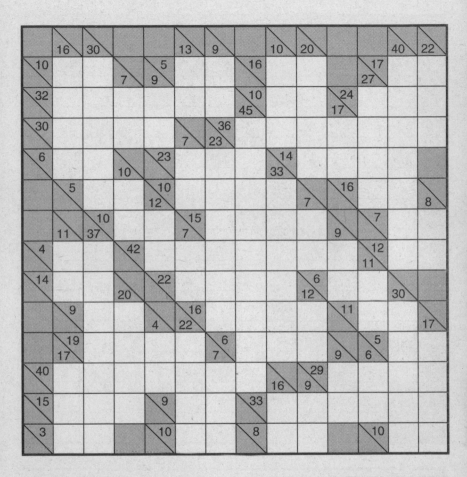

Scratch pad:

Kakuro 33

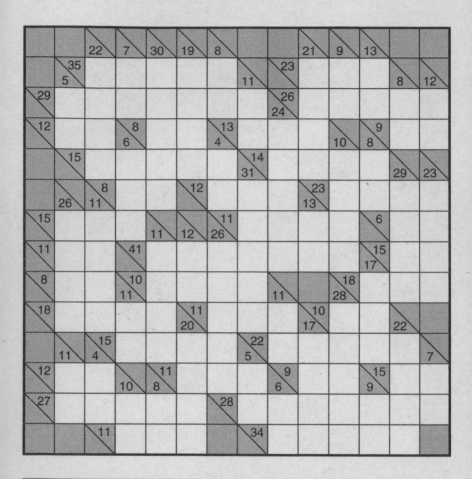

Scratch pad:

Kakuro 34

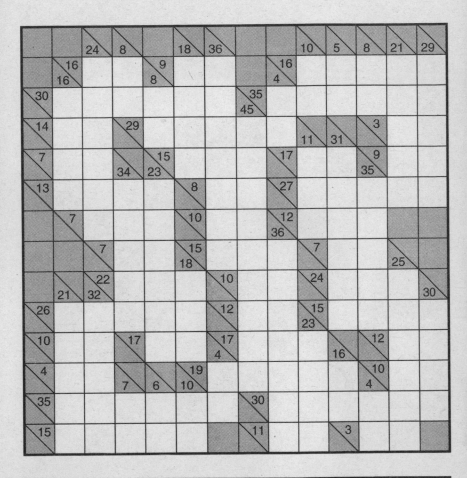

Scratch pad:

Kakuro 35

Kakuro 36

Scratch pad:

Kakuro 37

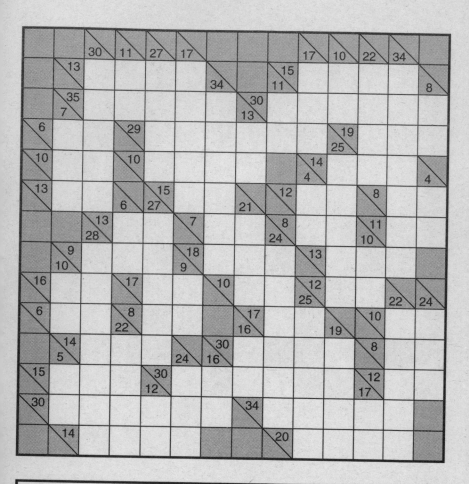

Scratch pad:

Kakuro 38

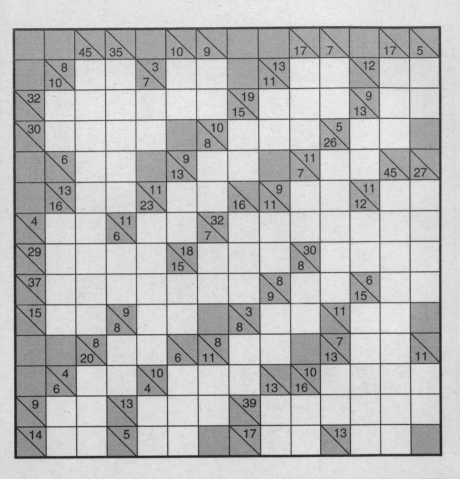

Scratch pad:

Volume 1   43

Kakuro 39

Scratch pad:

Kakuro 40

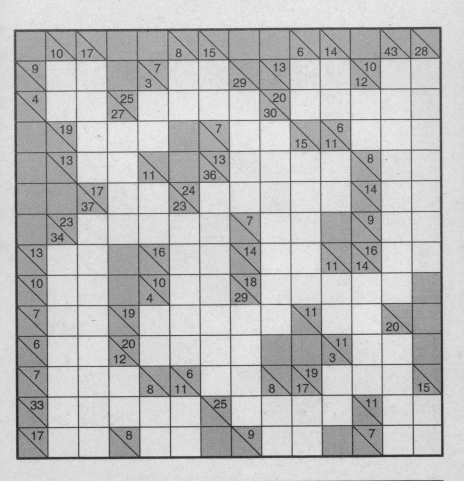

Scratch pad:

Kakuro 41

Scratch pad:

Kakuro 42

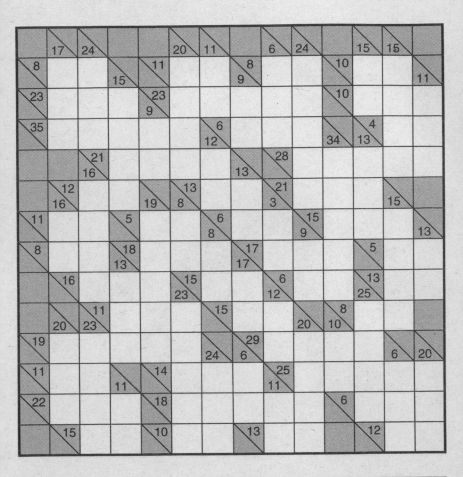

Scratch pad:

Kakuro 43

Scratch pad:

Kakuro 44

Scratch pad:

Kakuro 45

Scratch pad:

Kakuro 46

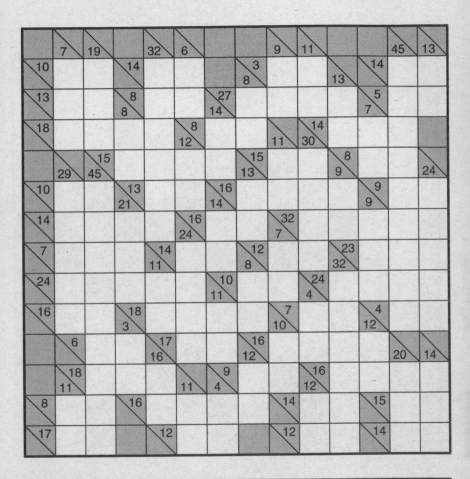

Scratch pad:

Kakuro 47

Scratch pad:

Kakuro 48

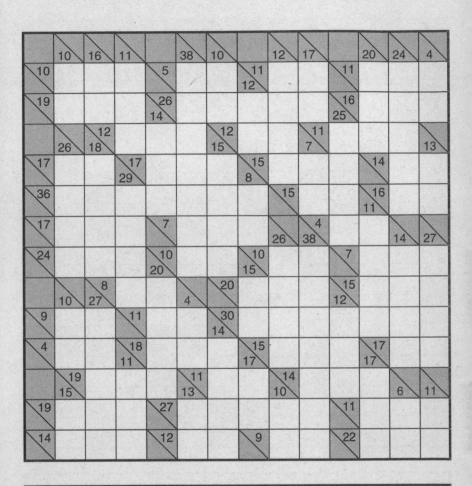

Scratch pad:

Kakuro 49

Scratch pad:

Kakuro 50

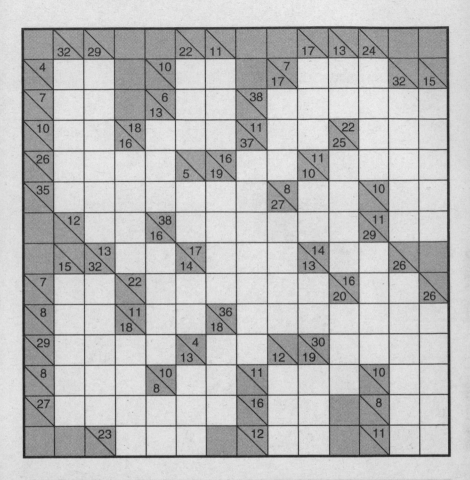

Scratch pad:

Kakuro 51

Scratch pad:

Kakuro 52

Scratch pad:

Kakuro 53

Scratch pad:

Kakuro 54

Scratch pad:

Kakuro 55

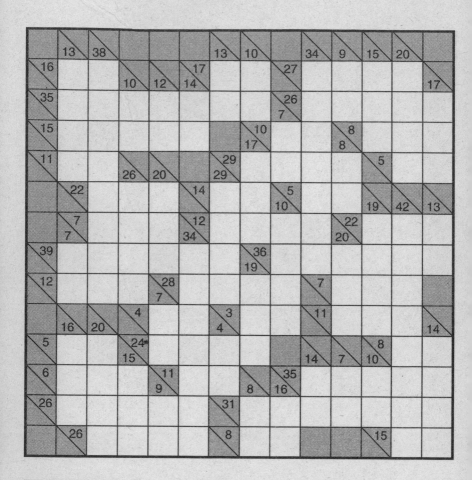

Scratch pad:

Kakuro 56

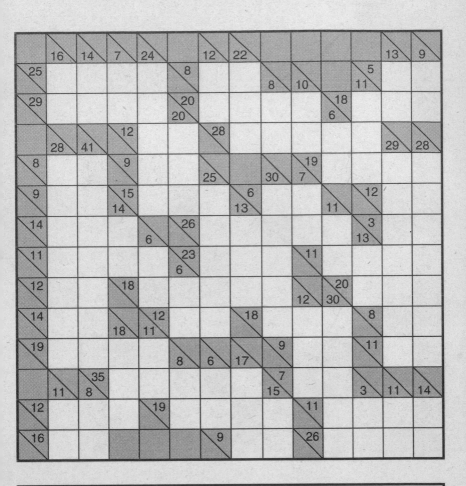

Scratch pad:

Kakuro 57

Scratch pad:

Kakuro 58

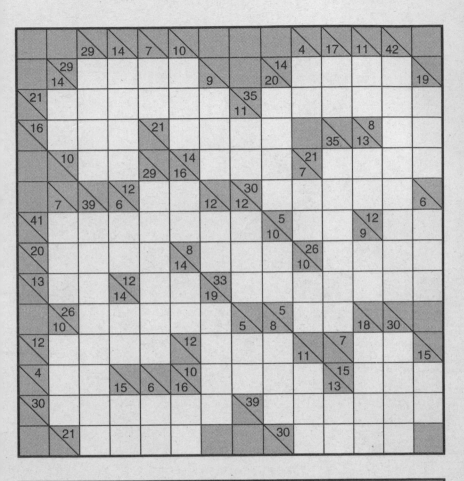

Scratch pad:

Kakuro 59

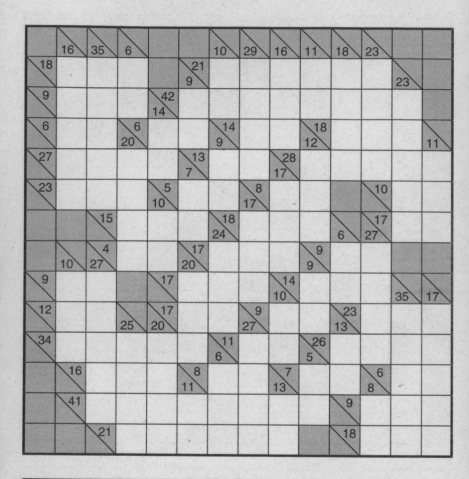

Scratch pad:

Kakuro 60

Scratch pad:

Kakuro 61

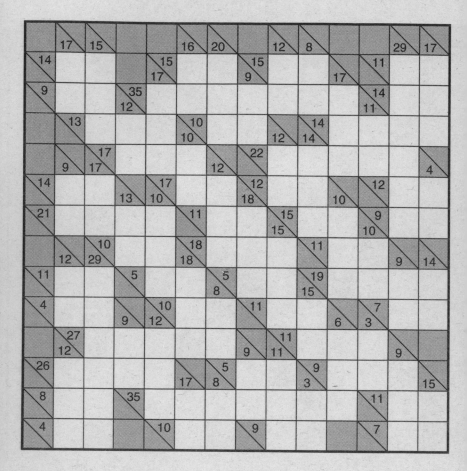

Scratch pad:

Kakuro 62

Scratch pad:

Kakuro 63

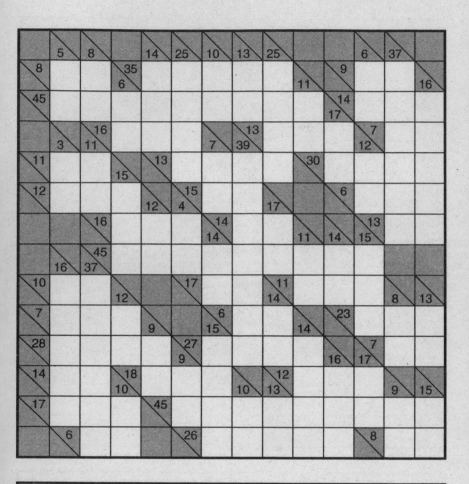

Scratch pad:

Kakuro 64

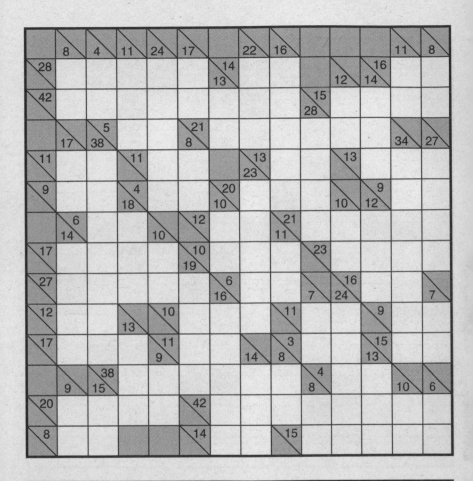

Scratch pad:

Kakuro 65

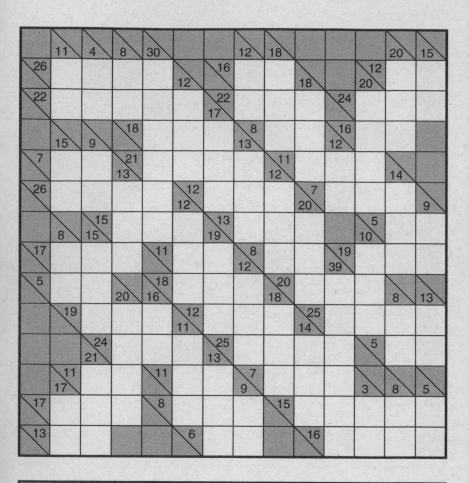

Scratch pad:

Kakuro 66

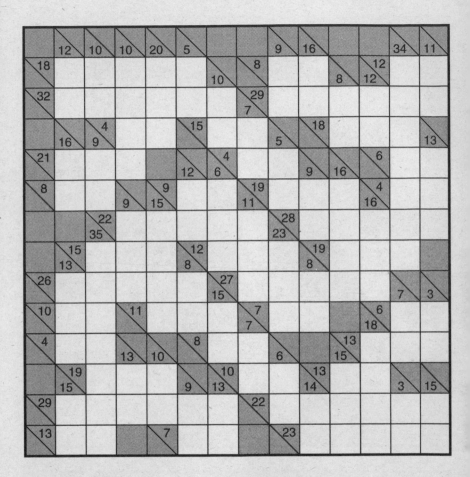

Scratch pad:

Kakuro 67

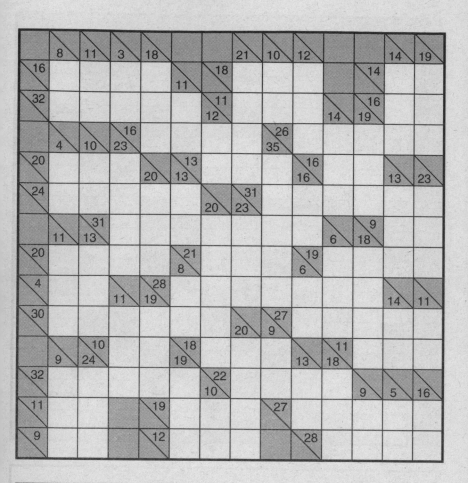

Scratch pad:

Kakuro 68

Scratch pad:

Kakuro 69

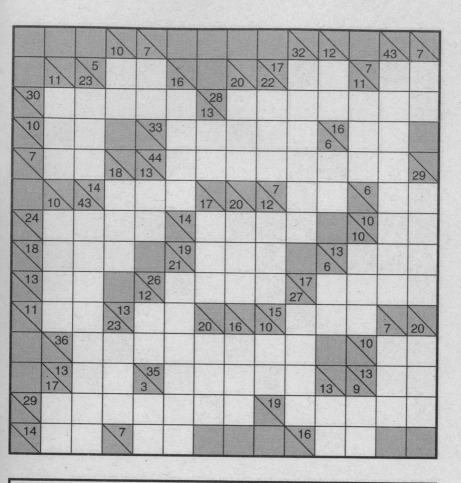

Scratch pad:

Kakuro 70

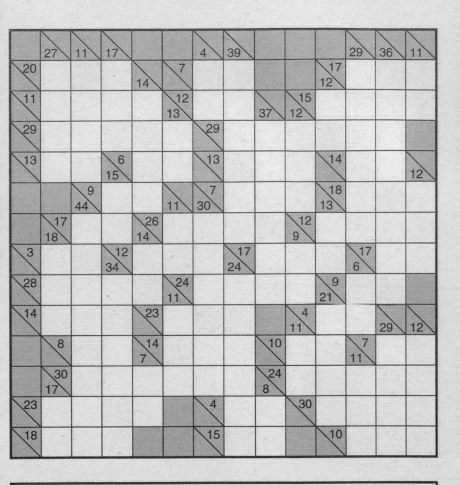

Scratch pad:

Kakuro 71

Scratch pad:

Kakuro 72

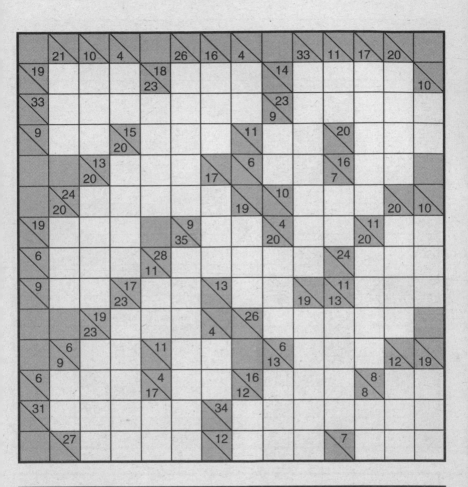

Scratch pad:

Kakuro 73

Scratch pad:

Kakuro 74

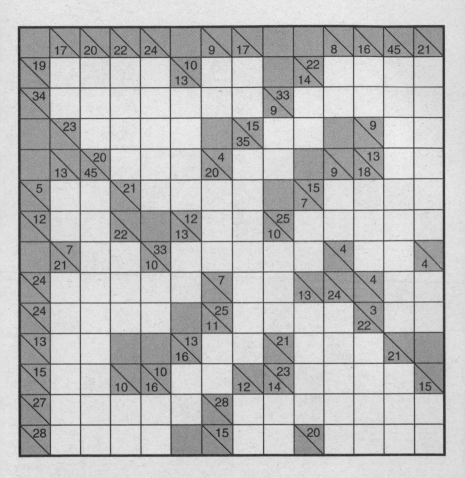

Scratch pad:

Kakuro 75

Scratch pad:

Kakuro 76

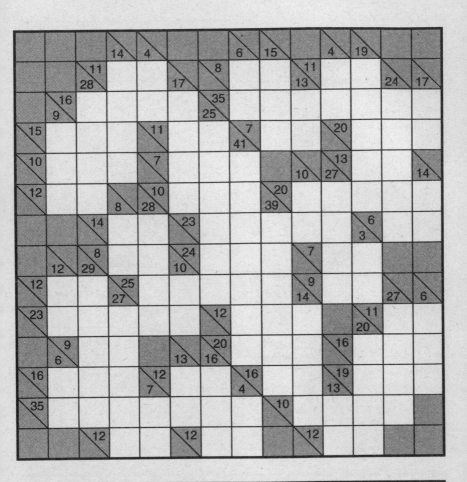

Scratch pad:

Kakuro 77

Scratch pad:

Kakuro 78

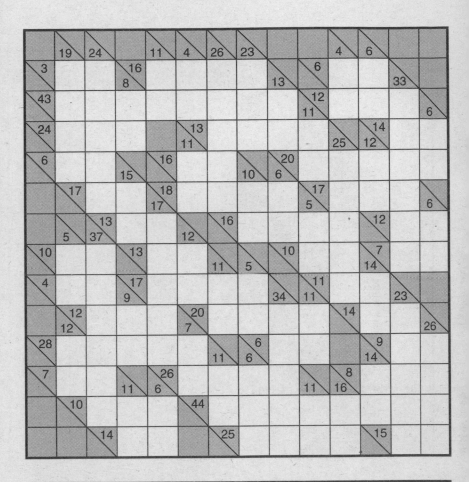

Scratch pad:

Kakuro 79

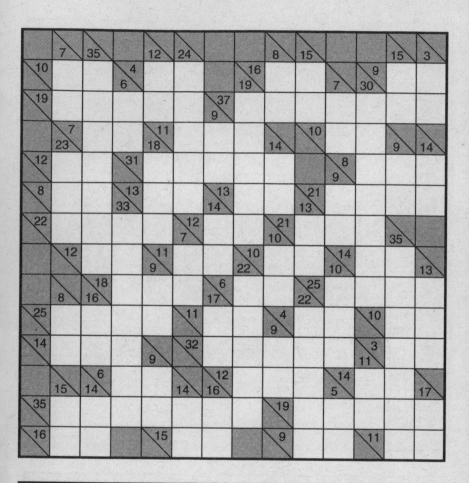

Scratch pad:

Kakuro 80

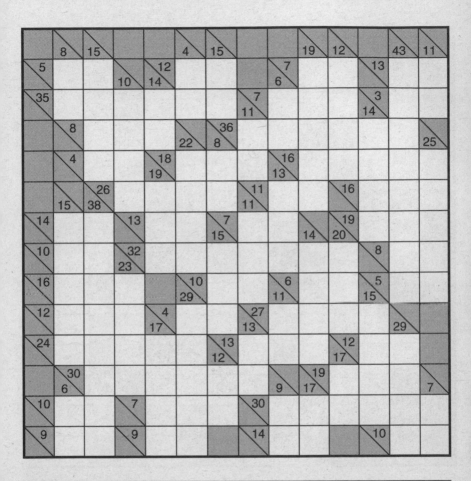

Scratch pad:

Kakuro 81

Scratch pad:

Kakuro 82

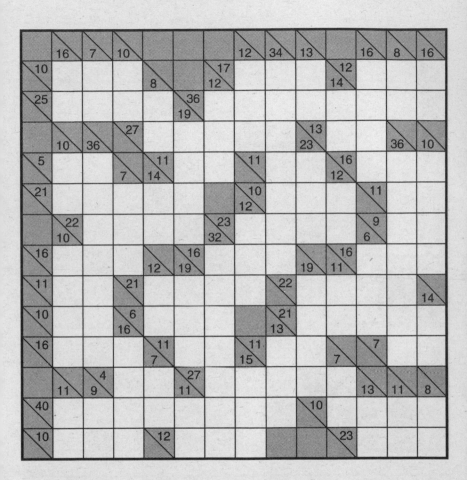

Scratch pad:

Kakuro 83

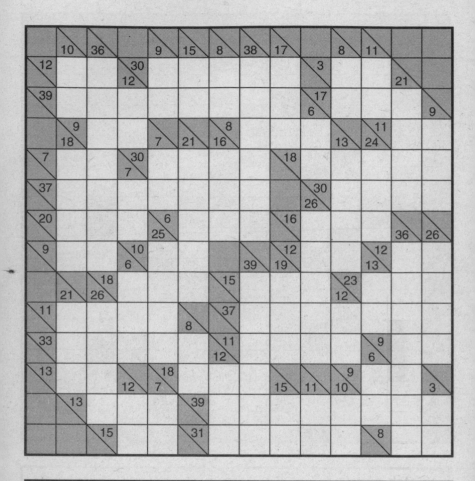

Scratch pad:

Kakuro 84

Scratch pad:

Kakuro 85

Scratch pad:

Kakuro 86

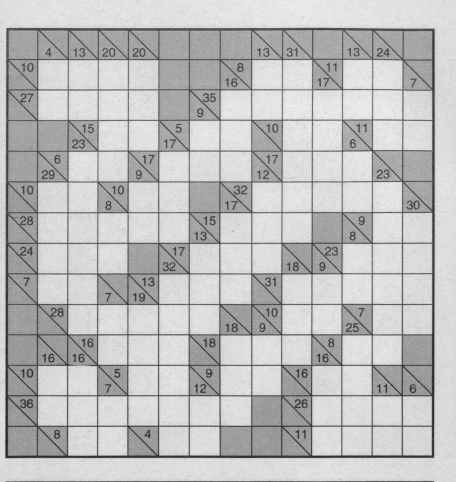

Scratch pad:

Kakuro 87

Scratch pad:

Kakuro 88

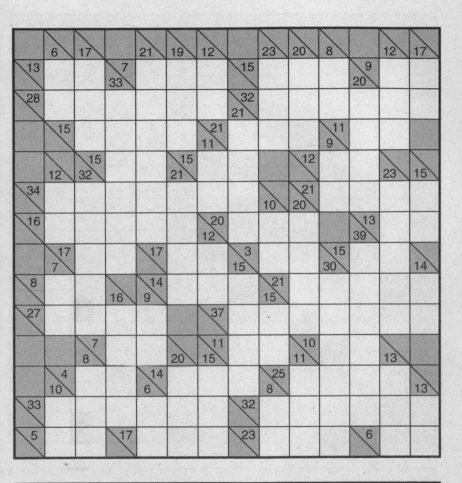

Scratch pad:

Kakuro 89

Scratch pad:

Kakuro 90

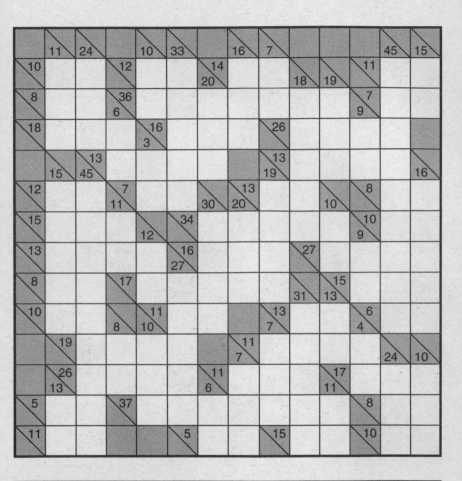

Scratch pad:

Kakuro 91

Scratch pad:

Kakuro 92

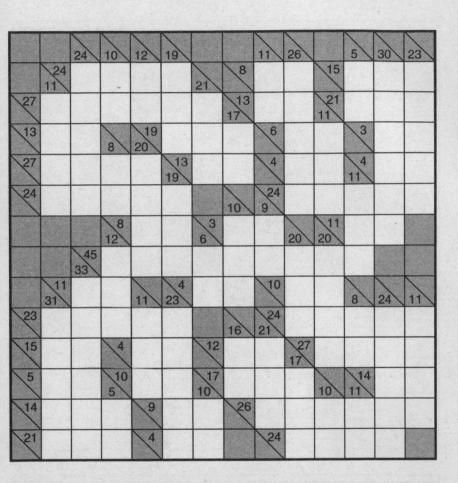

Scratch pad:

Kakuro 93

Kakuro 94

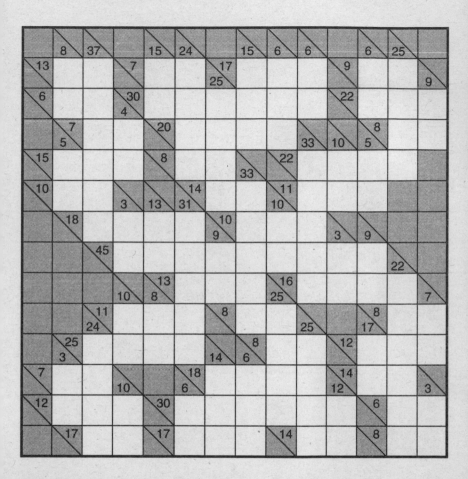

Scratch pad:

Kakuro 95

Scratch pad:

Kakuro 96

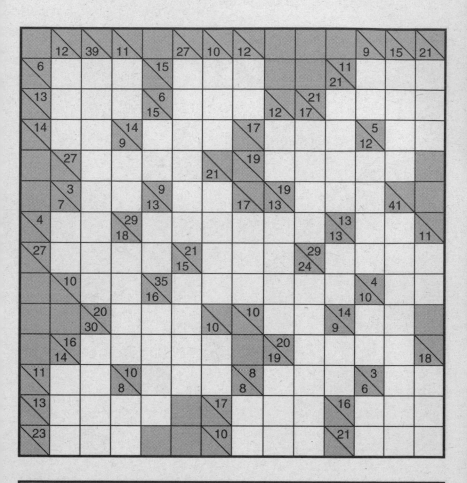

Scratch pad:

Kakuro 97

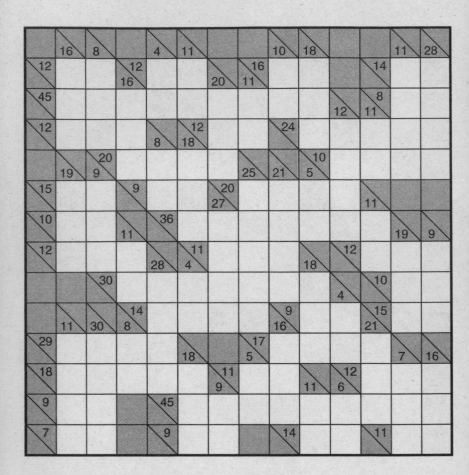

Scratch pad:

Kakuro 98

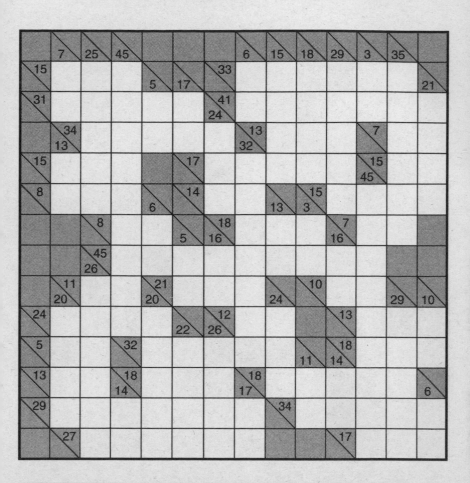

Scratch pad:

Kakuro 99

Kakuro 100

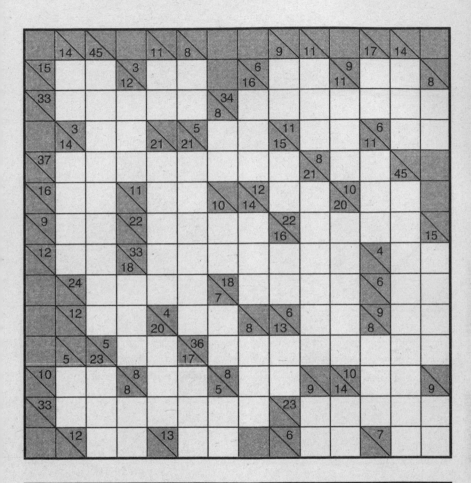

Scratch pad:

Kakuro 101

Scratch pad:

Kakuro 102

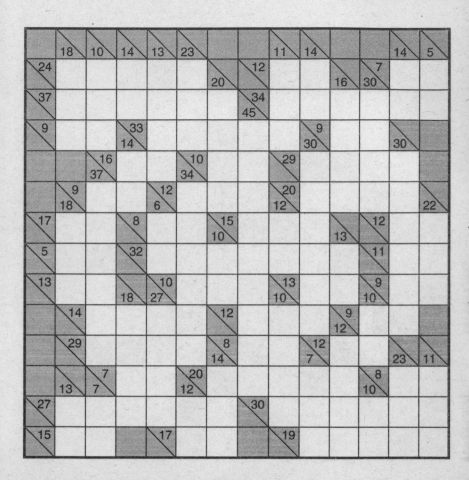

Scratch pad:

Kakuro 103

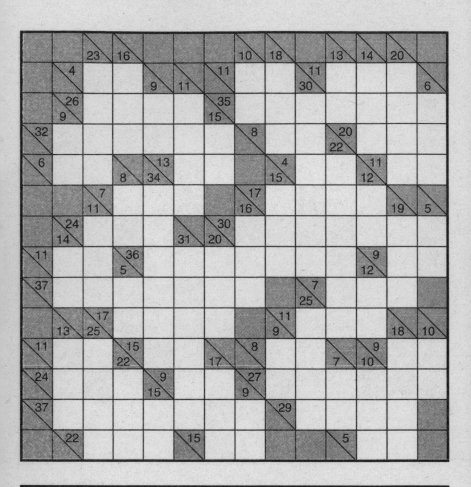

Scratch pad:

Kakuro 104

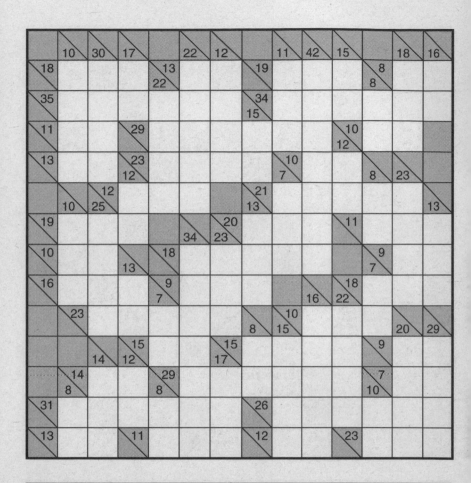

Scratch pad:

Kakuro 105

Scratch pad:

Kakuro 106

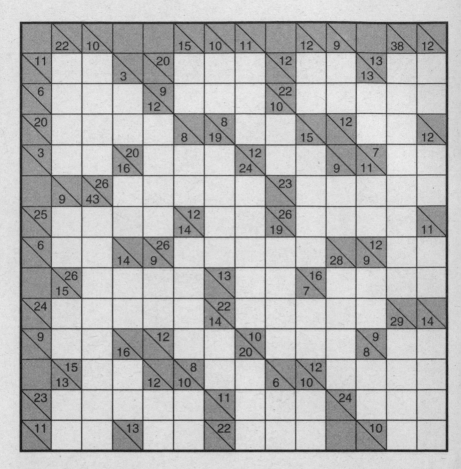

Scratch pad:

Kakuro 107

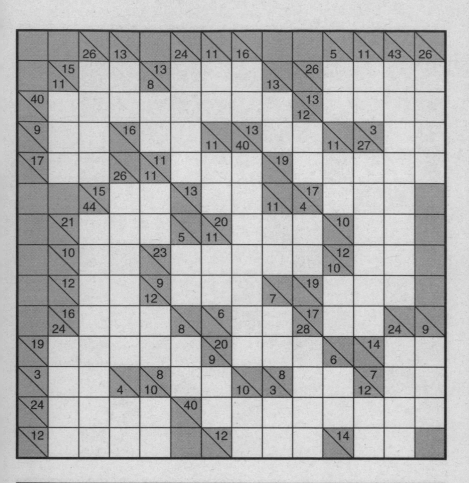

Scratch pad:

Kakuro 108

Scratch pad:

Kakuro 109

Scratch pad:

Kakuro 110

Scratch pad:

Kakuro 111

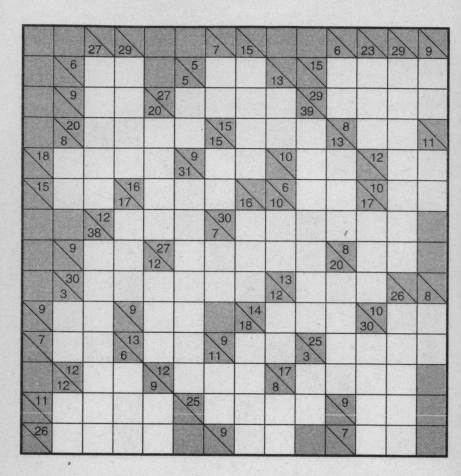

Scratch pad:

Kakuro 112

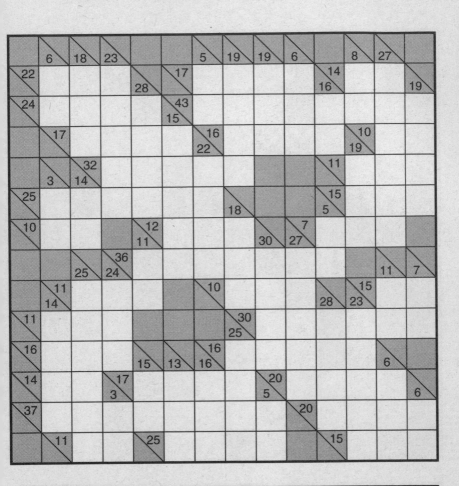

Scratch pad:

Kakuro 113

Scratch pad:

Kakuro 114

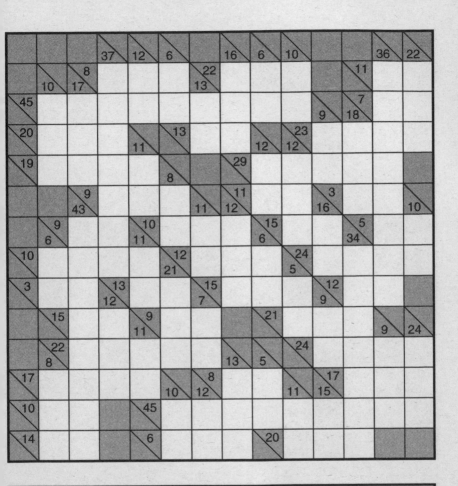

Scratch pad:

Kakuro 115

Scratch pad:

Kakuro 116

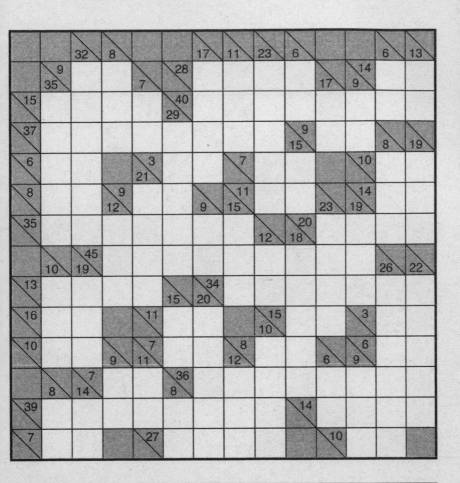

Scratch pad:

Kakuro 117

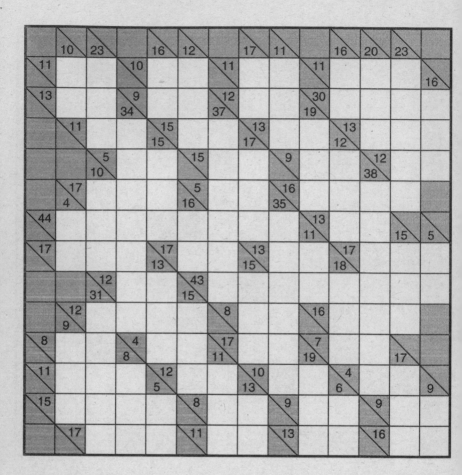

Scratch pad:

Kakuro 118

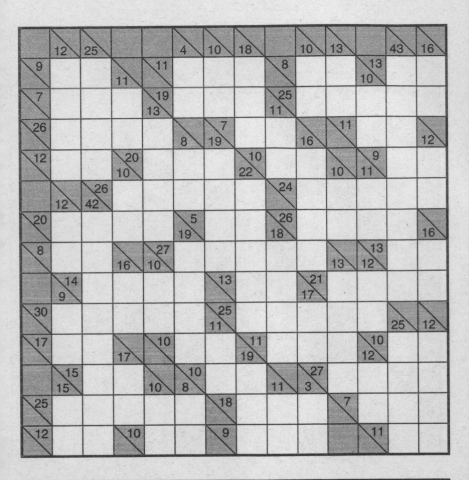

Scratch pad:

Kakuro 119

Scratch pad:

Kakuro 120

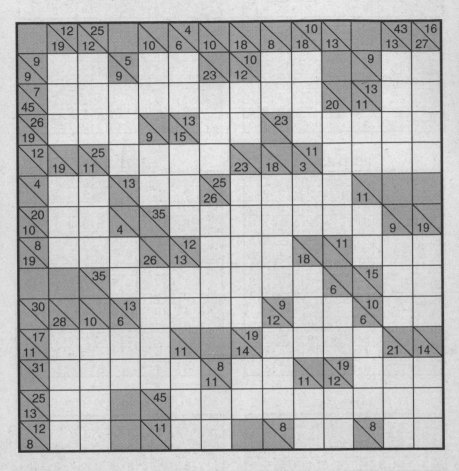

Scratch pad:

PUZZLE 1

PUZZLE 2

PUZZLE 3

PUZZLE 4

PUZZLE 5

PUZZLE 6

PUZZLE 7

4	5				1	4			1	2	9	
7	3		5	7	3	8		1	2	6	8	9
2	1	4	6	3		9	7	3	8		7	5
	4	8			9	7	1	2	3		5	2
3	6	9	5	7	8			5	9	1		
2	9		1	2		8	9	4		8	9	3
4	8	9			1	9	7			9	7	2
1	2	4		1	9	7		8	1		8	5
		1	9	6			7	9	8	6	4	1
6	9		4	3	1	8	9			1	3	
1	8		8	4	7	9		9	5	7	6	8
4	3	6	1	2		1	3	7	9		5	4
	4	9	2			2	9			1	9	

PUZZLE 8

1	2	9	7	3			2	9		1	2	
3	4	6	5	2	1		1	4	5	8	9	7
		8	6		7	5	6		2	6	8	4
	2	1			6	9	8	2		3	7	
1	8		3	2	8		9	7		2	6	
3	9		5	3	9			3	9			
	6	5	2	1	3		8	6	1	7	9	
	4	1			7	9	5		4	9		
2	8		9	8		9	8	2		2	6	
7	6		7	9	8	1			3	1		
1	4	9	6		4	7	2		3	1		
3	5	2	4	7	1		3	5	7	6	8	9
3	1		8	3			4	1	2	3	8	

PUZZLE 9

	8	9	7	5		8	3		9	6	2	7
9	7	8	1	3		4	1		6	8	4	9
3	2	1		2	9		9	4	3	2	1	
	6	5		1	3	7	6	9	8	5		
9	5	2	8		1	2		6	2	1		
4	3		1	2		3	6		9	1		
2	1		4	5	1	2	8		4	9		
	4	2		7	6		5	7		2	1	
	3	7	1		9	7		9	1	5	8	
	1	3	2	5	8	9	7		9	8		
	1	4	8	3	9		1	6		2	3	1
9	4	8	6		1	8		8	1	4	6	9
7	2	6	9		2	9		9	8	5	7	

PUZZLE 10

6	8	9	1	7	4			7	8	5	9	
4	7	5	3	6	2	1		2	3	1	7	9
	5	2			8	4	9			3	7	
8	9		9	8	5	2	6			2	4	
7	3		8	1	6		9	2	3	1		
6	2	1	5		9	1		3	1	2		
9	1	3	6		7	9	8		4	9	2	7
	2	4	1		7	9		3	8	1	5	
	9	8	7	4			5	2	9		9	8
8	5			6	9	4	1	8		7	9	
9	2			1	7	3			1	5		
1	3	2	4	6		8	1	2	4	5	3	6
	1	9	6	8			2	6	5	9	8	7

PUZZLE 11

1	8	4		4	3	7			1	3	5	2
8	9	6		2	1	3	9		6	9	7	3
		9	7	1		1	7	3	8		3	1
	9	7	2			2	8	9		8	9	5
7	3	8		7	2	9			2	1		
9	4		6	2	1	8		7	9		3	5
5	1		9	8	3		3	1	6		6	8
3	2		8	1		3	1	2	8		4	9
		3	2			2	8	4		6	2	1
4	2	8		3	2	1			8	3	1	
1	4		2	7	1	4		9	3	1		
3	9	8	4		4	8	2	1		9	7	8
2	5	3	1			9	8	3		8	1	2

PUZZLE 12

8	3				5	6	8			2	4	1
7	1	6	2	8	9	3	4	5		6	8	9
5	2	3	8	9	7	4		8	1		6	8
9	4			6	8	9	1		3	1	9	7
		5	1	4			2	3	9	4		
5	3	7	2			9	3	1			2	8
7	2			9	3	8	4	2			4	9
9	1			7	2	1			6	9	1	3
		6	9	8	4			7	1	2		
9	7	1	2		1	8	6	9			5	9
8	9		1	5		9	4	5	3	8	1	7
7	2	9		7	9	6	1	8	4	3	2	5
3	1	2			1	3	2				3	8

PUZZLE 13

	9	4		7	6	8	9			9	5	
	7	2		2	1	6	8	9		5	4	3	1
	2	1	3			1	2	8	9	6		4	9
	8	3	9	2	1			7	3		1	6
			8	9	5		3	5	1		8	9
		1	4			3	1		7	1		8	9
	6	5		1	5	4		3	8	4		7	6
	9	8		4	2		6	7			9	2
		4	8		3	2	1		4	2	6	
		6	9		6	4			7	1	8	3	6
	6	9		1	8	9	2	4			1	2	4
	1	3	2	4		8	7	9	2	5		1	9
		7	9				9	8	6	7		5	8

PUZZLE 14

	1	9			2	7			3	8	1	7	9
	7	8	4	9	5	6			1	5	2	3	4
		4	2	6	7	3	8	1		9	3
	3	2		2	4		9	3			7	2	1
	7	5		7	1	2		7	8		9	8	5
	8	6		5	3	1	2		1	7	8
		1	8	3		9	7	4		6	5	4
			3	1	4		6	8	5	9		6	2
	4	1	2		7	1		6	9	8		9	4
	7	3	9			9	7		7	3		8	1
		7	9		8	2	4	6	1	9	3
	2	1	4	6	3			7	3	2	5	1	4
	7	3	5	8	9			9	8			2	9

PUZZLE 15

		5	7		5	9			1	5		2	8
	2	1	9	3	4	5	7		4	3	2	6	9
	9	2		6	9		1	5			3	1
	8	7	5	9		6	9	8	1			3	1
		4	6		9	2		9	5	2	8	7	6
	7	9		2	1		9	3		4	9
	5	8		9	2	5	3	6	7	1		9	1
		1	8		9	5		9	5		5	6
	8	1	3	6	9	7		7	2		9	3
	9	7		4	1	2	9		8	1	2	4
		4	3		8	1		9	5		7	9
	5	8	6	4	2		9	7	8	6	3	1	2
	7	9		8	1		9	2		9	8

PUZZLE 16

	1	7		4	9	8	7			4	5
	9	6	8		1	5	3	2			8	9
	7	2	3	1		7	2		8	9	1	2	4
		7	9	3	2	1		6	3	1		8	9
		3	5	2	1		4	5	1			1	8
	7	9		4	5	6	1		7	6	1	
	4	8	2	5	3	1		1	4	7	2	6	9
		9	6	4		1	4	9	8		3	1
	7	2		9	7	5		2	3	1	5
	9	7		1	6	8		3	5	1	2	4
	4	1	2	9	8		4	2		9	7	8	2
	6	1			8	6	7	9		8	9	6
	9	6		9	8	1	7		3	7

PUZZLE 17

	2	7		3	4	1		6	1		9	4
	3	8		7	9	5		7	2		2	3	1
	1	5			2	6	8	9		7	8	2
	8	9	2	1	3		1	9		1	8
			8	6	9		1	8	7	9	2	3
		9	5	3	7	8	1		4	9		8	9
	1	8			9	2	1				1	8
	3	4		7	1		5	4	6	8	7	9
	2	7	6	9	5	1			1	3	2
			8	4		9	2		7	9	8	5	6
	1	8	9		9	8	1	2				7	9
	2	3	1		2	7		9	6	8		1	3
	3	9			1	5		7	9	4		2	1

PUZZLE 18

	3	5	8		8	5	7	9		6	1
	4	5	8	9		3	2	1	4	6	7	5
	8	7	9		7	9			1	3	8	2
		4	6		1	4			2	8	9	3
	8	2			3	6		1	7			9	2
	3	1	6	7			2	7	8	1		8	1
			8	9		2	1	9		9	7
	3	9		2	1	4	9			8	5	4	2
	4	6			7	9		2	8			3	6
	1	7	3	2			1	6		7	2
	7	9	8	4			5	9		9	7	8
	5	8	6	3	1	2	4		9	8	5	2
	2	5		8	6	7	9		8	3	1

PUZZLE 19

```
 2 3 1 . . 4 9 . . 9 4 5
 8 9 3 1 . 1 3 6 8 9 5 2 7
 . 9 7 6 5 . 1 2 4 . .
 1 2 . 8 1 . 1 2 9 . 9 3
 7 8 9 . . 2 8 . 5 3 2 1
 . 3 8 . 1 6 . 7 9 8 6 4
 5 9 . 6 7 3 8 4 5 2 . 8 2
 7 1 2 3 9 . 7 9 . 7 8
 8 7 5 9 . 4 9 . . 3 8 9
 9 8 . . 1 2 3 . 1 4 . 1 5
 . . 7 8 9 . 3 7 9 8
 5 9 4 1 2 3 8 6 . 3 1 4 2
 7 8 2 . . 1 6 . . 3 2 6
```

PUZZLE 20

```
 . . 9 5 . 7 9 1 . . 1 2 4
 6 9 5 4 7 3 8 2 . 5 9 8
 3 6 2 1 4 . 8 9 7 2 4
 . 8 2 . 9 3 . 8 9 3 7
 2 9 . 7 3 2 1 6 5 . 3 8
 6 8 1 2 9 . 5 2 . 4 2 1 9
 . 2 6 . 1 6 9 . 8 9
 4 1 8 9 . 4 7 . 2 6 7 8 3
 9 3 . 1 7 9 8 4 6 . 3 4
 7 3 8 9 . 9 1 . 6 2
 5 2 7 8 9 . 7 8 6 9 4
 9 8 4 . 6 4 9 2 7 5 3 1
 4 2 1 . 8 1 2 . 9 7
```

PUZZLE 21

```
 9 8 7 5 . . 9 1 2 . 5 4
 5 7 4 1 2 3 . 8 6 7 9 3 2
 4 2 1 . 8 9 6 1 . 3 2 1
 8 4 . 9 7 8 2 . 1 9 . 4 3
 6 3 . 2 1 7 . 6 8 9 1
 7 1 . . 1 3 . 1 2
 . 6 1 . 2 1 9 . 6 7
 . 8 7 . 2 7 . 3 5
 . 1 9 8 6 . 2 8 6 . 9 6
 4 6 . 6 2 . 2 3 7 9 . 1 8
 1 2 4 . 1 7 5 9 . 1 2 3
 2 3 8 7 6 9 . 1 2 3 4 5 7
 3 4 . 3 1 7 . 6 7 8 9
```

PUZZLE 22

```
 . 7 5 6 9 8 . . 3 2 6 9
 1 3 2 5 4 7 8 . 2 1 4 3
 6 8 . 4 9 . 9 1 4 8 7
 3 4 . 3 8 2 . 8 6 . 9 1
 5 1 . 5 6 4 . 9 3 8 2
 6 9 8 1 . 3 9 5 8 1
 2 3 . 5 8 . 9 7 . 3 9
 . 7 3 2 8 9 . 5 3 1 4
 3 8 9 6 . 1 8 5 . 1 8
 1 4 . 9 2 . 8 3 1 . 7 9
 . 9 3 7 8 1 . 6 3 . 9 8
 4 3 1 2 . 3 6 4 9 2 7 5
 9 7 8 4 . 7 1 8 5 4
```

PUZZLE 23

```
 . 1 3 5 2 . 3 9 . . 6 2
 . 6 9 8 7 . 1 2 7 3 8 9 5
 5 2 . 9 6 . 5 7 9 8 . 6 1
 1 3 2 . 5 9 8 . . 1 5 8 6
 . 7 6 . 9 8 . . 1 4 2
 1 5 . . 7 5 8 4 2 6 9
 8 9 1 . 5 1 4 . . 1 7 9
 . 8 5 2 4 6 7 9 . . 5 2
 . 9 6 8 . 7 9 . 2 3
 9 8 2 3 . 2 6 8 . 8 6 7
 6 7 . 5 9 8 7 . 1 4 . 8 1
 8 5 7 4 1 6 3 . 3 9 8 2
 . 6 9 . 5 1 . 2 5 3 1
```

PUZZLE 24

```
 9 4 . 8 1 9 . 1 9 . 9 4
 7 5 8 9 6 3 4 . 5 1 9 7 2
 . 9 1 . . 7 9 . 3 2 1
 5 7 6 2 . 6 1 8 . 8 3
 3 8 2 . 9 7 . 3 8
 2 3 1 . 8 3 5 . 1 3 9
 1 6 . 7 3 1 2 4 6 9 . 5 2
 . 9 4 1 . 1 2 9 . 2 4 1
 . 9 3 . 3 8 . 1 7 8
 4 9 . 1 5 8 . 1 3 8 9
 2 4 1 . 2 9 . 2 8
 1 5 3 8 9 . 6 7 5 8 9 3 4
 3 2 . 1 7 . 5 9 7 . 1 2
```

PUZZLE 25

PUZZLE 26

PUZZLE 27

PUZZLE 28

PUZZLE 29

PUZZLE 30

KAKURO PUZZLES

2	4	3	1		8	4				8	9	7
3	8	4	2		5	1	4			6	4	5
	7	1		5	1		7	9	1		9	4
	9	6		9	3		3	5		2	4	1
8	3	2	1			3	8		9	7	8	2
9	5		8	2	1	5				5	3	
2	1	9		9	8	6	1	3		1	9	7
		6	9			9	4	7	1		6	3
2	9	8	7		4	7			9	5	2	1
1	4	2		3	5		4	8		9	7	
4	8		9	1	2		2	9		6	1	
	7	9	2		1	7	9		1	7	4	2
	3	2	1			1	5		7	8	5	9

2	8			4	1		7	9			8	9
5	7	1	2	9	8		2	8		8	9	7
8	9	6	7			8	1	2	9	7	3	6
1	5			6	8	9		1	8	3	2	
	1	4		1	2	4	3			9	7	
	6	4		4	3	7	1			6	1	
3	1		8	4	3	7	9	6	5		5	7
8	6			3	5	6	8		4	2		
	8	1			1	2	4	9		9	2	
	7	9	1	2		1	2	3			4	1
7	9	8	3	6	2	5			7	5	9	8
9	4	2		5	4		9	8	2	1	7	6
1	2			9	1		7	1			8	2

	7	6	8	9	5			9	6	8		
2	5	1	6	4	3	8		7	3	5	2	9
3	9		7	1		3	9	1			6	3
	1	2	4	5	3		7	4	1	2		
		3	5		1	9	2		3	6	9	5
9	5	1				3	1	5	2		5	1
8	3		2	9	6	7	5	8	4		7	8
6	2		1	3	2	4				1	8	9
3	1	9	5		1	8	2		1	9		
		2	3	1	9		9	2	3	7	1	
9	3			2	8	1		1	8		9	6
2	1	8	7	9		4	2	6	7	3	5	1
	2	1	8			4	8	9	6	7		

	9	7		2	7			3	1	2	6	4
2	4	1	6	8	9		1	7	4	6	8	9
9	5		2	7	8	9	3				2	1
4	3			1	6	8		8	9		1	8
1	2	7	3		2	6		2	6	8	4	7
	1	4	2		3	7		1	4	7		
		6	1		1	5	9		1	6		
	9	5	8		3	7		8	9	7		
6	7	8	4	1		4	8		3	5	1	6
2	8		8	9		2	6	9			4	8
1	3			3	1	2	4	9		3	7	
8	9	6	4	7	1		1	2	7	3	8	9
4	5	1	2	3			3	8		1	2	

	6	1		2	9		7	8	6	3	5	9
9	6	7	5	8		3	4	1	2	6	7	9
8	5	2	1	4			3	1		8	5	
7	2		6	7	5	9	8			2	4	8
	4	5			3	5	7		1	7		
	7	1			6	4		3	9		4	1
5	8	9		3	1	2	6	8		9	5	6
2	9		5	6		1	8			1	7	
		9	7		1	3	9			5	8	
6	9	2			3	6	4	2	1		2	7
5	8		3	9				7	2	1	3	8
4	5	6	2	8	9	7		8	4	7	6	9
	2	5	1	7	4	3		9	3		1	6

2	1		6	9		1	7		9	3	1	4
4	3	7	1	8		3	8	9	5	1	7	2
	5	8		1	9		6	1			8	9
1	2			7	1	2			8	5		
8	9	1	2			3	9	1		6	3	9
	9	3		8	4		7	4		2	8	
	3	1		9	5	2		7	1			
8	5		9	4		6	9		8	2		
4	1	3		1	9	8			9	8	1	2
	2	6			3	2	1				6	9
1	4		9	6		3	6		1	5		
6	8	3	4	5	2	9		5	1	4	9	3
7	9	1	3		1	3		4	9		8	1

PUZZLE 37

```
   2 3 7 1       9 2 3 1
   6 8 9 5 7   9 7 8 2 3 1
 1 5   8 3 6 9 2 1   8 4 7
 2 8   3 2 1 4     3 9 2
 4 9     6 9     3 9   7 1
     5 8   3 4   1 7   8 3
   6 1 2   8 9 1   1 3 9
 9 7   9 8   8 2   5 7
 1 5   7 1     8 9     2 8
   4 9 1     9 6 7 8   1 7
 4 3 8   8 9 7 3 2 1   3 9
 1 2 3 8 9 7   4 6 7 8 9
   1 2 4 7     1 3 9 7
```

PUZZLE 38

```
   2 6   1 2     9 4   9 3
 2 5 8 1 9 7   9 7 3   7 2
 8 7 9 6     7 2 1   4 1
   1 5   1 8     2 9
   6 7   4 7     1 8   5 6
 1 3   2 9   1 2 6 9 4 3 7
 7 8 5 9   1 8 9   6 8 7 9
 2 4 1 8 9 6 7   7 1   1 5
 6 9   3 6     2 1   2 9
     7 1   1 7     3 4
   3 1   1 2 7   4 1 2 3
 1 8   1 3 9   5 7 9 4 6 8
 5 9   3 2     8 9   5 8
```

PUZZLE 39

```
     9 7   1 8 3   1 2 8 4
 7 6 8 1 9 2 4 5   3 1 5 2
 1 7 6   7 8 9   1 5 4
   4 1   3 2 1 5 9   1 9
 9 8   4 2   3 5 2 7   6 5
 8 3   2 9   9 8   9 8
 2 1 3 8 7   6 9 3 2 1
   2 9   8 9   7 1   9 2
 8 9   6 3 1 2   4 2   4 3
 7 5   9 5 3 1 2   1 3
     4 5 1   9 8 6   9 7 1
 2 5 1 3   6 3 1 2 8 7 5 4
 9 8 2 1   9 8 3   1 2
```

PUZZLE 40

```
 7 2   1 6   4 9   6 4
 3 1   1 7 9 8   2 5 9 3 1
   8 9 2   5 2   3 1 2
   6 7   7 1 2 3   5 3
   8 9   2 9 4 1 8   8 6
   1 3 2 9 8   3 4   4 5
 7 6   7 9   9 5   9 7
 3 7   4 6   5 3 2 1 7
 4 3   1 2 3 7 6   9 2
 2 4   3 1 7 9     3 8
 1 2 4   1 5   2 8 9
 9 5 8 7 4   8 7 9 1   2 9
 8 9   1 7   1 8   1 6
```

PUZZLE 41

```
 3 7   1 9   7 3   3 8 9
 9 8   1 3 4 2 9 8   1 6 4
 2 5   2 8 6 5   2 6 8 9
   9 4 8 6   1 3   2 4
   2 6   1 3 8 2   9 7
   9 5   3 8   9 1 3   9 8
 7 8   9 2     4 9   6 2
 1 6   6 1 8   3 5   4 5
   2 1   6 5 9 2   1 3
   5 2   2 1   1 3 8 9
   9 8 6 3   4 7 8 9   1 2
 9 2 3   9 8 2 1 4 6   3 9
 4 1 2   2 1   2 3   2 8
```

PUZZLE 42

```
 1 7   2 9   1 7   8 2
 9 8 6   1 2 8 3 9   7 1 2
 7 9 5 6 8   1 2 3   3 1
   1 3 9 8   1 7 3 9 8
   9 3   4 9   4 8 9
 9 2   4 1   4 2   6 1 8
 7 1   9 7 2   1 7 9   1 4
   4 9 3   6 9   2 4   4 9
   1 2 8   8 7   6 2
 4 2 3 1 9   5 7 9 8
 7 4   2 7 5   5 1 9 2 8
 9 8 5   3 8 1 4 2   2 1 3
   9 6   1 9   7 6   3 9
```

132   KAKURO PUZZLES

PUZZLE 43

```
 . 6 1 . 9 3 1 . . . 7 3 9
 4 8 6 9 7 5 3 1 . 3 4 1 2
 1 5 . 8 1 . . 9 4 1 2 . .
 . 7 3 1 . 3 1 8 2 . 9 8 7
 8 4 1 2 . 9 5 . 3 2 . 6 1
 2 1 . . . . 3 9 1 6 8 . .
 . 2 7 . 9 6 . 6 7 . 7 3 .
 . 1 3 8 5 9 . . . . 7 1 .
 9 2 . 2 6 . 5 9 . 1 2 8 6
 2 1 6 . 2 8 1 3 . 2 8 9 .
 . 7 8 1 2 . . 5 9 . 5 1 .
 1 2 8 9 . 9 1 3 4 5 8 6 7
 3 7 9 . . 2 7 9 . 9 4 . .
```

PUZZLE 44

```
 3 9 7 . . 9 4 . 8 6 . 8 7
 6 8 9 . 9 8 7 4 5 3 1 2 6
 . 1 8 6 7 2 . 8 7 5 2 . .
 . 5 1 . . 1 7 9 . . 1 3 .
 2 8 . 9 3 . 2 9 . 9 2 3 8
 3 9 . 8 2 7 9 . 9 6 1 2 .
 1 7 9 . 1 3 8 9 4 . 9 7 1
 . 3 1 9 8 . 7 8 2 9 . 9 3 .
 9 2 3 8 . 9 4 . 1 7 . 8 2
 2 1 . . 9 2 3 . . 3 4 . .
 . 9 3 2 1 . 8 7 1 3 9 . .
 7 9 8 6 4 3 5 2 1 . 2 8 9
 2 7 . 4 1 . 4 1 . . 1 7 3
```

PUZZLE 45

```
 2 1 . 2 9 . 1 7 . 4 7 2 .
 6 5 . 1 7 . 3 8 . 8 9 3 1
 . 2 6 . 4 7 . 6 7 . 8 5 3
 . 7 9 . 5 1 . 1 8 . 7 9 .
 . 9 4 2 . 9 7 . 3 6 9 1 .
 4 6 2 1 5 8 9 7 . 1 8 . .
 8 2 1 . 1 6 . 8 9 . 2 1 8
 . 8 1 . 3 2 4 1 6 5 7 9 .
 . 5 9 7 8 . 4 9 . 1 3 9 .
 3 4 . 9 5 . 1 3 . 9 4 . .
 1 7 2 . 2 8 . 5 3 . 1 7 .
 4 8 1 2 . 3 8 . 7 2 . 1 4 .
 . 9 4 5 . 1 4 . 9 3 . 3 9
```

PUZZLE 46

```
 2 8 . 9 5 . . 1 2 . . 5 9
 4 9 . 7 1 . 6 8 9 4 . 1 4
 1 2 7 8 . 6 2 . . 9 1 4 .
 . 1 2 4 8 . 9 6 . 6 2 . .
 7 3 . 5 8 . 6 2 7 1 . 7 2
 3 2 8 1 . 9 7 . 9 8 2 6 7
 2 1 4 . 9 5 . 4 8 . 6 9 8
 8 4 9 2 1 . 7 3 . 9 1 8 6
 9 7 . 9 6 2 1 . 3 4 . 3 1
 . 5 1 . 8 9 . 9 1 2 4 . .
 . 9 2 7 . . 8 1 . 3 8 4 1
 2 6 . 9 2 1 4 . 8 6 . 7 8
 9 8 . . 9 3 . . 4 8 . 9 5
```

PUZZLE 47

```
 7 9 . 4 8 9 . 9 6 . 8 3 9
 1 7 . 1 2 8 . 8 1 . 2 1 4
 . 2 1 9 . 3 2 1 . 9 2 . .
 . 2 7 . 1 3 9 5 7 . . . .
 3 1 9 . 2 9 . . 7 1 . 4 9
 8 5 . 2 4 5 6 3 1 . 6 1 3
 . 2 9 . 2 8 1 . 7 4 . . .
 9 8 4 . 6 8 9 7 4 5 . 5 1
 7 2 . 9 7 . . 9 2 . 1 9 7
 . 7 2 8 5 3 . . 1 9 . .
 . 4 8 . 2 7 1 . 5 2 9 .
 2 1 3 . 5 9 . 9 3 8 . 1 4
 8 2 9 . 1 8 . 8 1 2 . 2 9
```

PUZZLE 48

```
 2 7 1 . 4 1 . 2 9 . 8 2 1
 8 9 2 . 5 9 3 1 8 . 9 4 3
 . 8 1 3 . 9 3 . 7 3 1 . .
 9 8 . 9 7 1 . 6 1 8 . 8 6
 2 1 5 4 9 8 7 . 6 9 . 9 7
 7 2 8 . 2 4 1 . . 1 3 . .
 8 7 9 . 8 2 . 9 1 . 2 1 4
 . 7 1 . 6 5 9 . 5 2 8 . .
 7 2 . 8 3 . 9 4 2 5 1 3 6
 3 1 . 9 1 8 . 8 6 1 . 8 9
 . 9 8 2 . 2 9 . 7 6 1 . .
 9 8 2 . 4 1 8 9 5 . 7 1 3
 6 7 1 . 9 3 . 1 8 . 9 5 8
```

PUZZLE 49

7	9		9	1	3			3	8	9		
2	3	9	7	5	8	1		1	2	8	6	4
		5	1		9	8	6			6	4	2
1	4			6	7	9	8			1	3	
2	1		9	3		7	1	9	8		1	2
	9	8	4		3	5		7	1		7	6
	2	1		7	2		3	2		1	2	
9	5		3	6		7	6		6	9	5	
2	3		5	9	7	6		6	8		9	7
	8	9			1	3	9	7			8	1
9	7	4			8	9	7		1	5		
5	6	2	9	4		1	3	2	4	7	6	9
		1	2	3			1	7	9		1	6

PUZZLE 50

3	1			8	2			1	4	2		
5	2			5	1		6	7	9	8	5	3
7	3		1	9	8		2	9		9	8	5
8	9	2	7			7	9		1	5	3	2
9	6	1	5	2	4	8		1	7		9	1
	8	4		3	6	5	7	9	8		7	4
		9	4		7	1	9		9	5		
3	4		1	5	2	4	3	7		9	7	
2	6		2	9		9	8	6	3	7	1	2
5	8	7	9		1	3			9	8	6	7
1	5	2		1	9		1	2	8		4	6
4	9	1	2	3	8		7	9			5	3
		8	6	9			4	8			3	8

PUZZLE 51

2	8		9	7		5	8			8	5	
5	6	3	2	1	4	7	9			7	2	9
8	9	6	5	3	7			1	7		1	8
1	4		8	2			3	5	9	7	8	
	1	3			8	5			1	9		
		4	9		8	9	6	3		2	7	9
3	8		5	7	6	4	2	1	8		4	5
9	7	2		9	4	2	1		3	7		
	3	1			5	1			8	1		
	9	7	8	5	2			4	8		3	1
4	1		7	2			6	3	5	7	9	8
9	2	3			9	6	1	2	4	3	8	5
	5	7			7	3		1	3		6	2

PUZZLE 52

		9	8	3			2	7	9		8	3
8	9	4	3	2	1		3	5	7	6	9	8
1	8			9	8	1	4		2	6	1	
	7	4			6	1		1	9		7	2
	3	1	9	7			9	2	4	1		
9	4		8	1		9	1	3		8	1	
3	2	9	1		8	1	3		1	9	2	4
	1	8		8	1	3		9	3		7	8
		1	2	7	3		1	2	7	9		
9	3		1	6		7	8			5	6	
1	2	9		2	6	1	4			3	5	
7	5	8	6	4	9		2	9	4	6	8	3
3	1		2	9	8		8	6	2			

PUZZLE 53

	9	6	7	8		6	2			8	9	
9	8	2	1	4		1	4	5	9	8	6	7
4	1		6	7	8	9		2	5	1	3	
		1	2	3	6	8	9		1	6		
	9	4		6	9		1	3		7	1	
	8	2	9		1	6		1	3	9	6	8
9	3		1	3	2	4	8	7	9		2	1
2	1	4	3	5		1	9		1	2	8	
	2	5		1	9		1	5		3	9	
		9	7		4	8	3	2	5	1		
1	4	3	2			9	5	7	8		1	8
7	9	8	6	2	1	3		4	6	2	8	5
2	8			9	4			8	9	7	5	

PUZZLE 54

8	7		2	1	3	5			2	9	3	
1	2	3	9	5	7	8		9	2	6	8	5
6	8	9		7	9		2	5	1		3	1
7	5		2	6		3	1		4	1	2	
	1	2	9	8		9	1			6	2	
4	9	7		9	3	1		5	2			
1	3	6	7		8	2	1		3	9	8	6
	5	1		5	4	1		7	1	9		
	1	8		1	8		2	5	8	6		
1	2	9		7	9		3	9		3	2	
2	7		7	9	8		1	4		2	5	9
5	9	7	6	1		2	3	7	1	6	9	8
3	8	2			7	8	9	6		2	1	

134   KAKURO PUZZLES

	7	9				8	9		3	8	7	9
2	3	7	8	9	5	1		2	1	6	8	9
1	2	3	4	5			2	8		2	1	5
3	8					8	5	9	7		2	3
	6	9	7		9	5		4	1			
	1	2	4		5	4	2	1		7	6	9
6	5	8	9	4	7		3	7	9	8	5	4
1	4	7		7	8	9	4		4	1	2	
			1	3		2	1		7	3	1	
4	1		6	9	1	8					7	1
3	2	1		8	3			9	6	7	8	5
9	8	6	2	1		7	9	5	1	3	4	2
	9	8	7	2		1	7				9	6

9	6	2	8		3	5				4	1
7	8	5	9		9	8	1	2		1	9	8
		4	8		9	7	8	1	3		
2	6		2	7				5	7	4	3
4	5		1	5	9		5	1			8	4
1	4	9			1	2	8	6	9		1	2
3	2	5	1		6	8	9		2	5	3	1
5	7		5	1	2	3	7			8	5	7
6	8			5	7		1	8	9		2	6
7	9	1	2					1	8		6	5
	8	9	6	5	7		3	4			
2	1	9		2	1	9	7		2	1	3	5
9	7				1	8		7	2	8	9

6	2			1	5			1	4	2
7	3		9	2	4	8		1	2	8	9	4
9	6	7	8	1	3		1	7	9		6	1
8	4	1		6	9	7	8				7	3
5	1		2	3	5	1		1	9	2	3	
		1	9				1	2	7	8	5	9
7	4	9		3	6		9	3		1	2	6
1	2	4	3	8	9				1	9	
	1	2	8	9		8	2	4	5		9	6
3	9			3	4	1	2		8	4	2
5	8		5	1	9		8	9	7	5	6	3
1	6	3	9	8		2	7	8	1		8	1
2	7	9			4	9			7	4

	9	8	5	7			1	8	3	2	
6	5	3	2	1	4		2	3	9	8	6	7
8	7	1		2	3	7	9			5	3
	8	2			2	4	8		7	4	1	9
		5	7			1	5	8	9	7	
2	5	4	8	9	7	6		2	3		9	3
1	8	2	9		5	1	2		9	7	8	2
4	9		4	8		5	8	7	6	2	4	1
	4	9	2	6	5		3	2			
4	2	5	1		9	2	1			1	6
1	3			4	3	2	1		2	7	6
5	7	6	2	9	1		5	4	6	7	8	9
	1	9	4	7			6	7	8	9	

	4	9	5			4	5	2	6	1	3	
2	6	1		8	6	7	9	5	2	4	1
1	5		5	1		9	5		7	9	2
3	7	8	9		5	8		9	8	7	3	1
6	8	9		1	4		7	1			8	2
		2	7	6		7	9	2			9	8
		1	3		7	9	1		5	4	
1	8			7	9	1		4	1	9	
3	9			9	8		4	5		8	9	6
6	7	9	8	4		5	6		8	6	7	5
	2	8	6		1	7		2	5		5	1
	1	6	5	7	2	9	8	3		1	6	2
	2	1	4	3	6	5			7	8	3

3	7			9	8		4	1			1	5
2	1	9		1	5	8	9	2		1	2	6
	2	3	1	7		9	7		1	2	4
4	8		2	5		6	1		2	9	8
3	4		8	7		8	1	3	7	9	6
6	9	3	1		2	9		2	7		7	1
	9	7	5	1	3	2	6	8	4	
9	7		2	1		1	5		9	1	8	7
7	6	8	5	2	9		1	2			6	1
	8	9	4		8	1		1	5		9	2
	5	7	3		7	9		3	2	7	1
8	3	5		4	1	2	8	9		9	2	1
6	1			9	6		1	8			4	9

PUZZLE 61

	9	5			9	6		9	6			4	7
	8	1		9	7	5	8	3	2	1		5	9
		9	3	1		9	1			7	4	2	1
			9	7	1			3	2	9	7	1	
	6	8			9	8		9	3			9	3
	3	9	4	5		3	8		9	6		8	1
		9	1		1	9	8		3	8			
	9	2		4	1		1	4		1	2	7	9
	3	1		9	1		3	8			2	5	
		9	2	1	8	7			7	3	1		
	9	8	7	2			4	1		1	2	6	
	2	6		9	8	7	5	3	1	2		2	9
	1	3			9	1		7	2			1	6

PUZZLE 62

	3	8		3	2		6	1			9	6	2
	1	3	2	8	6	5	7	4		9	2	5	1
	5	9	4		5	1		9	7	2		8	4
	2	4		5	1			3	2			7	3
			9	1		9	5			6	8	1	
		1	4			8	1		6	7	9	3	8
	1	3			7	1		5	7			4	9
	7	6	8	5	9		6	9			3	9	
		4	1	9			1	7		1	4		
	5	9			2	8			7	3		2	7
	3	8		3	7	9		9	3		6	1	5
	1	5	6	9		5	6	4	1	3	9	7	8
	2	7	9			7	8		4	9		3	9

PUZZLE 63

	1	7		5	9	7	6	8			1	8	
	4	1	5	2	6	3	7	9	8		5	6	3
			1	7	8			1	3	9		5	2
	2	9			2	1	3	7		8	9	7	6
	1	2	9			6	9				3	2	1
			4	9	3		5	9				9	4
		2	3	1	5	6	8	7	9	4			
	3	7			9	8		4	5	2			
	1	2	4			1	5			9	6	8	
	4	9	8	7		3	7	9	8			2	5
	6	8		2	7	9			2	1	9		
	2	6	9		2	1	4	5	3	6	8	7	9
		5	1			2	6	8	1	9		2	6

PUZZLE 64

	2	3	6	8	9		8	6				9	7
	6	1	4	5	8	7	9	2		9	3	2	1
		1	4		6	5	1	4	3	2			
	9	2		6	5		4	9		9	1	3	
	8	1		1	3		9	3	8		2	7	
		5	1		8	4		7	2	1	3	8	
	1	6	8	2		2	1	7		8	2	4	9
	2	7	9	8	1		2	4			9	7	
	4	8		2	1	7		5	6			8	1
	7	9	1		9	2			2	1		9	6
		9	8	7	3	5	6		3	1			
	7	9	3	1		4	1	2	6	9	8	7	5
	2	6			6	8		2	5	4	3	1	

PUZZLE 65

	8	3	6	9		7	9				4	8	
	3	1	2	7	9		5	8	9		8	9	7
			8	1	9		1	7		9	7		
	6	1		3	2	7	9		2	8	1		
	9	8	7	2		1	3	8		4	2	1	
			5	1	9		1	3	9			4	1
	7	9	1		2	9		1	7		2	9	8
	1	4			1	8	9		4	9	7		
		2	8	9		2	1	9		8	1	7	9
		9	7	8		2	8	9	6		1	4	
	9	2		2	9		1	2	4				
	9	7	1		1	3	4		3	5	1	2	4
	8	5			1	5		7	2	6	1		

PUZZLE 66

	4	3	2	8	1		1	7			3	9	
	8	7	3	9	4	1		8	9	1	3	6	2
		1	3		9	6			7	9	2		
	9	8	4			1	3				5	1	
	7	1		7	2		2	8	9		1	3	
		6	8	5	1	2		1	4	6	8	9	
	9	2	4		3	1	8		2	8	9		
	9	8	1	2	6		8	9	7	1	2		
	3	7		1	2	8		6	1			4	2
	1	3			7	1				9	3	1	
		2	9	8		6	4		8	5			
	7	1	4	2	6	9		2	5	4	3	1	7
	8	5			3	4		9	3	1	2	8	

PUZZLE 67

2	4	1	9			9	7	2			6	8
6	7	2	8	9		7	3	1			7	9
			1	2	9	4		9	6	8	1	2
3	8	9			3	1	9		7	9		
1	2	4	8	9			8	9	1	2	5	6
		2	3	4	1	8	6	7			1	8
2	1	8	9		5	9	7		2	1	7	9
1	3			1	2	6	5	4	3	7		
8	9	1	2	7	3			2	1	8	9	7
		2	8		9	7	2			2	5	4
6	7	8	9	2		9	7	5	1			
2	9			9	7	3		8	9	2	1	7
1	8			8	3	1		8	7	4	9	

PUZZLE 68

	7	8		1	7			7	9		9	4
9	4	7	1	2	5		3	4	8	9	1	5
8	3		5	7		6	9		2	7		
2	1			4	9	2		3	1	5	6	
4	2	1		6	2		3	8		6	8	9
	5	9			1	8		6	4	1	2	
		5	7		1	7	9		1	2		
6	9	4	1		6	9				1	2	
1	8	3		1	5		9	7		8	9	6
	3	2	1	8		2	7	6			8	7
	6	2			8	6		4	9		7	2
2	1	7	8	4	9		7	2	3	6	5	1
9	7		9	2			6	5		4	6	

PUZZLE 69

			3	2			8	9		6	1	
8	9	7	5	1		4	5	2	3	1	7	6
2	8			4	7	9	8	5		7	9	
1	6			2	6	7	9	4	5	3	8	
		1	4	9			6	1		1	5	
1	6	8	9		2	4	1	7		3	7	
2	7	9			9	7	3		1	4	8	
4	9			3	6	9	8		1	2	5	9
3	8		9	4			3	5	7			
	1	8	3	2	6	5	4	7			2	8
	4	9		5	9	7	6	8			4	9
8	3	6	2	1	5	4		9	4	2	1	3
9	5		1	6				9	7			

PUZZLE 70

9	3	8			1	6			5	3	9	
3	2	5	1		3	9		8	4	1	2	
7	1	4	8	9		8	5	9	4	1	2	
8	5		2	4		5	6	2		8	6	
	6	3			4	2	1		9	7	2	
	8	9		9	2	7	8		4	2	5	1
1	2		9	2	1		7	1	9		8	9
8	6	9	5		6	1	9	8		5	4	
9	4	1		8	9	6		3	1			
	5	3		2	8	4		4	6		5	2
	9	8	6	1	4	2		7	5	1	8	3
9	7	6	1		3	1		7	8	9	6	
8	3	7			8	7			2	7	1	

PUZZLE 71

	9	5				2	1		5	2		
9	8	1		2	3	4	6	7	5	9	8	1
3	7		4	1	7	8	9		8	1		
1	3		9	4		1	7			7	1	
	4	9		8	1		2	4	1	9	8	
8	2	4	9		8	7	9	1	2	3		
2	1		2	8	9	6	7	3	1		6	2
		6	3	9	4	1	2		3	9	8	6
8	9	2	1	3			1	9		7	1	
1	4			8	4		2	9		9	6	
	5	8		7	3	6	1	8		5	9	
9	2	5	7	1	3	6	8	4		8	4	1
4	1		9	5					9	2		

PUZZLE 72

9	7	3		9	8	1		7	4	2	1	
4	2	1	9	8	6	3		9	7	4	2	1
8	1		7	6	2		5	6		3	8	9
		9	3	1		4	2		7	9		
	9	8	4	2	1		5	4	1			
9	8	2			7	2		1	3		9	2
3	2	1		1	9	8	7	3		9	8	7
8	1		8	9		9	4			8	2	1
	9	3	7			9	8	6	2	1		
	4	2		8	3			3	2	1		
2	3	1		3	1		7	5	4		1	7
7	9	5	8	2		3	4	2	1	7	9	8
	7	6	9	5		9	2	1		1	2	4

PUZZLE 73

8	4		9	1		1	7			5	2
2	3		8	7	1	2	9		1	2	8	9
1	2			9	2	4			2	8	9
	8	6			8	9	1	7	6		1	3
	1	3	5				2	9	8		2	8
7	9	4	8	2		3	9		4	8
1	7	2		7	5	1	6	9		9	3	7
		1	6		3	7		6	3	7	1	2
3	9		8	2	1			9	6	4
1	8		9	8	2	1	4		4	2
	2	5	1		6	8	1		8	2
1	4	9	2		7	8	9	2	1		9	4
3	1			3	9		8	5		7	1

PUZZLE 74

9	7	2	1		2	8			1	7	9	5
8	4	3	2	1	7	9		5	7	9	8	4
	9	8	4	2			6	9			6	3
	9	8	3		1	3				7	6
4	1		9	7	3	2			1	8	4	2
9	3			8	4		2	8	9	5	1
	2	5		4	9	8	7	5		1	3
1	4	8	2	9		6	1			1	3
2	5	9	8		9	2	6	8		2	1
5	8			8	5		4	9	8
6	9		7	3		2	4	9	8
3	6	2	7	9		5	6	1	2	3	4	7
4	7	8	9			7	8		1	2	9	8

PUZZLE 75

	3	1	2	5		2	7			8	4
	9	4	7	8		1	3		1	2	7
9	2		1	2	3	8	6	9		9	3	8
7	1	9		1	7	9		1	3		7	9
		3	8	9		1	3		8	3	1	2
8	9	1	3	6		6	1			9	6
1	5		1	3	4	7	5	9	8		4	1
	8	1		2	4		6	1	3	9	8
5	7	9	8		1	3		8	2	9
8	6		2	1		5	9	7		1	9	7
2	4	6		7	9	2	5	4	3		6	1
4	3	9		8	6			2	1	5	7
7	1			4	8			5	6	9	8

PUZZLE 76

	8	3			1	7		3	8
	4	2	1	9		5	6	8	1	2	4	9
4	8	3		5	6		2	5		3	9	8
2	7	1		1	2	4			5	8
3	9		2	3	5		3	5	1	2	9
	6	8		1	2	4	7	9		1	5
	2	6		9	7	8		6	1
9	3		5	2	4	8	6		7	2
3	2	1	9	8		6	5	1		9	2
	7	2			9	7	4		7	8	1
1	8	7		7	5		9	7		9	7	3
5	9	8	4	6	2	1		2	4	1	3
	9	3		9	3			9	3

PUZZLE 77

	8	1		1	9	8	2			2	7
7	9	1	3	6	5	4		2	5	9	8	7
9	8	6		7	2		9	7			9	1
5	2		8	5		9	4			9	7	2
	7	3	1			8	1		9	3	4
		8	9	4	2	1			3	1	2	6
3	9			9	8	2	4	1			1	2
6	8	9	4			6	8	3	1	2
	7	8	1		4	3			2	9	1
9	2	1			1	7		1	9		6	8
7	3			4	9		1	6		3	4	1
3	1	2	4	8		3	4	9	7	1	8	5
		7	9			1	2	8	3		9	6

PUZZLE 78

2	1		4	1	2	9			1	5
5	4	1	7	3	6	8	9		3	1	8
8	9	7			1	6	4	2		9	5
4	2			7	9		9	3	5	2	1
	8	9		4	8	1	5		9	7	1
	6	7		9	1	2	4		7	5
4	6		4	9			3	7		6	1
1	3		2	3	8	4		2	9
	9	2	1		3	1	7	9		5	9
9	8	7	3	1		4	2			2	7
3	4		6	8	3	9			5	1	2
	7	2	1		3	2	6	4	7	9	5	8
	9	5			1	8	7	9		6	9

138   KAKURO PUZZLES

PUZZLE 79

	4	6		3	1			7	9			8	1
3	1	4	9	2		9	1	6	4	8	7	2	
		5	2		8	2	1			3	7		
8	4			8	9	7	2	5			2	1	5
6	2			9	4		4	9		1	3	8	9
9	8	4	1		9	3			9	8	4		
	9	3			6	5		6	4		5	9	
		9	8	1		2	4		7	1	8	9	
7	9	8	1		8	3		3	1		7	3	
1	7	6			9	7	8	6	2		2	1	
		1	5		9	1	2		9	5			
8	5	2	4	6	9	1		4	3	2	1	9	
7	9			8	7			7	2			3	8

PUZZLE 80

1	4		3	9			5	2			4	9	
7	8	4	9	1	6		2	4	1		1	2	
	2	1	5			2	4	7	6	8	9		
	1	3		8	1	9		1	3	2	6	4	
		2	8	9	7		9	2		1	8	7	
5	9		9	4		6	1			3	7	9	
4	6		2	1	5	4	3	8	9		5	3	
3	4	9			9	1		2	4		3	2	
2	3	7		3	1		8	3	7	9			
1	2	4	9	8		9	3	1		3	9		
	1	3	5	9	8	4			9	2	8		
2	8		1	2	4		3	9	8	1	5	4	
4	5		2	7			6	8			7	3	

PUZZLE 81

	5	4	3	8		9	3			8	3	
1	3	7	4	9	8	6	2	5		7	2	
8	2			4	3		5	9		9	7	
	1	8	9			8	1		8	2	1	3
		2	1	8	9	7		3	5		5	9
9	1		2	3	8	6	9	1		1	6	
7	3	1		2	3	8			6	8	1	
	7	3		7	1	2	3	6	4		9	5
6	2		5	2		1	2	9	8	4		
9	4	8	6		2	9			9	7	1	
	9	7		9	3		3	9			6	2
	6	9		3	1	7	2	5	6	9	8	4
	5	4			4	9		1	2	7	9	

PUZZLE 82

7	1	2			1	7	9		1	2	9
9	6	8	2		1	3	8	4	5	2	6	7
		6	1	3	8	9		9	4		
4	1			3	8		2	9		9	6	1
6	2	1	5	7			1	6	3		8	3
	3	2	9	8		2	4	8	9		7	2
3	9	4			4	9	3			3	9	4
4	7		9	8	3	1		9	8	2	3	
2	8		3	2	1		7	3	1	2	8	
1	6	9		9	2		9	2			1	6
	1	3		9	8	3	1	6				
6	8	2	4	9	7	3	1		1	4	3	2
5	1	4		2	6	4				9	8	6

PUZZLE 83

9	3		4	8	5	6	7		1	2	
1	2	4	5	7	3	8	9		7	9	1
	1	8			5	1	2			9	2
1	6		6	8	9	7		4	2	8	3	1
7	8	4	1	3	5	9			7	9	8	6
8	9	3		1	2	3		8	1	7	
2	7		8	2			9	3		3	9
		2	9	7		4	9	2		9	6	8
5	3	1	2		7	8	6	9	4	1	2
9	8	3	6	7		5	2	1	3		2	7
7	6			1	8	9			1	8	
	9	3	1		3	8	7	4	1	5	9	2
	9	6		1	6	8	7	9		7	1

PUZZLE 84

	1	9		7	3		4	1			1	2
	6	7	9	8	5	4	2	3	1		7	5
9	3		4	1		9	8	6	5	1	4	
6	2		8	2		1	3			3	8	
	5	4		6	1			1	6	9	8	
	9	3		3	1		1	3		5	1	
2	8		7	6	4	2	1	8	9		2	3
1	7		8	1		4	8		4	7		
8	9	6	1			2	1		9	1	
	5	1		2	1		2	6		2	1	
	2	3	6	9	8	7		4	3		3	9
9	3		1	4	3	2	7	9	8	5	6	
6	1		7	1		1	8		1	5	

PUZZLE 85

PUZZLE 86

PUZZLE 87

PUZZLE 88

PUZZLE 89

PUZZLE 90

140 KAKURO PUZZLES

```
.  .  2  7  .  .  3  2  .  1  6  9  .
.  1  8  9  .  1  9  7  .  2  8  7  9
.  3  4  6  1  2  .  .  1  9  .  2  8
2  9  .  9  7  5  1  6  .  7  9  1  3
.  .  9  3  .  .  6  5  .  .  1  8  .
.  9  1  2  8  .  2  6  .  .  2  9  3
5  1  .  .  1  7  .  4  9  .  .  8  1
7  3  2  .  .  9  5  .  2  7  5  1  .
.  .  8  1  .  .  2  6  .  .  3  1  .
5  1  9  2  .  6  4  5  1  8  .  9  4
6  3  .  .  8  5  .  .  7  9  4  2  1
.  9  1  2  5  .  3  1  9  .  9  8  7
.  .  5  8  9  .  9  8  .  .  7  1  .
```

```
.  1  6  9  8  .  .  6  2  .  1  6  8
1  2  4  3  9  8  .  5  8  .  4  8  9
5  8  .  .  2  9  8  .  4  2  .  2  1
3  9  7  8  .  4  9  .  3  1  .  1  3
2  4  1  9  8  .  .  .  9  8  1  4  2
.  .  1  7  .  1  2  .  .  2  9  .  .
.  9  2  4  5  6  7  3  1  8  .  .  .
.  9  2  .  .  1  3  .  8  2  .  .  .
3  2  1  8  9  .  .  9  8  1  4  2  .
8  7  .  1  3  .  7  5  .  9  7  8  3
4  1  .  2  8  .  9  7  1  .  .  9  5
7  6  1  .  2  7  .  9  7  4  3  2  1
9  8  4  .  1  3  .  .  9  6  8  1  .
```

```
.  9  8  4  .  .  2  4  .  8  2  1  .
8  7  2  1  9  .  6  8  .  9  8  2  1
9  2  .  .  1  3  7  9  8  2  .  6  9
2  1  9  .  2  9  .  7  9  .  .  8  6
.  .  2  1  8  .  9  1  2  .  3  9  7
1  3  8  2  .  6  7  .  6  8  1  .  .
5  9  .  4  7  9  .  6  1  3  .  9  4
.  .  3  7  9  .  4  8  .  9  7  3  1
7  9  1  .  6  3  1  .  8  2  1  .  .
1  3  .  .  5  1  .  9  4  .  9  7  8
4  7  .  6  8  9  4  2  1  .  .  2  9
2  1  7  9  .  8  7  .  9  1  2  8  6
.  2  1  5  .  6  1  .  3  1  9  .  .
```

```
6  7  .  6  1  .  9  3  5  .  1  8  .
2  4  .  9  8  6  4  2  1  .  5  9  8
.  6  1  .  9  8  2  1  .  .  .  7  1
4  8  3  .  6  2  .  .  9  8  4  1  .
1  9  .  .  9  5  .  8  2  1  .  .  .
.  3  1  8  6  .  4  1  5  .  .  .  .
.  2  5  7  6  8  9  4  1  3  .  .  .
.  .  1  3  9  .  7  2  6  1  .  .  .
.  2  1  8  .  7  1  .  .  2  6  .  .
1  8  7  9  .  .  7  1  .  8  3  1  .
1  6  .  .  2  1  8  7  .  9  5  .  .
2  9  1  .  1  3  2  9  8  7  .  4  2
8  9  .  5  9  3  .  9  5  .  7  1  .
```

```
.  .  6  1  9  .  8  4  .  2  8  5  .
1  3  7  2  4  8  6  9  .  1  3  2  8
2  1  8  .  .  1  9  3  8  6  .  1  3
4  7  9  .  3  6  .  .  2  8  1  6  9
.  .  1  6  8  9  4  2  .  9  7  8  .
4  1  .  2  6  .  9  5  .  .  9  3  .
5  6  .  8  9  1  .  9  1  8  .  4  2
7  5  .  .  9  7  .  3  5  .  3  1  .
.  4  1  2  .  8  1  7  4  6  9  .  .
8  9  7  4  1  .  .  6  2  .  5  6  8
3  7  .  9  8  3  2  1  .  .  1  2  9
4  8  5  3  .  7  6  2  5  8  3  1  4
.  2  4  1  .  4  1  .  1  9  2  .  .
```

```
2  1  3  .  4  2  9  .  .  1  2  8  .
1  4  8  .  2  1  3  .  1  8  3  9  .
9  5  .  6  1  7  .  9  1  7  .  1  4
.  7  8  9  3  .  .  3  2  4  1  9  .
.  2  1  .  8  1  .  .  8  9  2  .  .
1  3  .  8  9  3  2  1  6  .  4  9  .
6  9  7  5  .  9  8  4  .  9  5  7  8
.  8  2  .  9  8  7  2  5  4  .  1  3
.  .  8  9  3  .  .  6  4  .  9  5  .
.  6  1  4  2  3  .  .  9  7  1  3  .
2  9  .  2  1  7  .  5  1  2  .  2  1
3  7  2  1  .  .  7  8  2  .  2  6  8
9  8  6  .  .  .  1  6  3  .  4  8  9
```

PUZZLE 97

9	3		3	9			7	9			5	9
5	4	6	1	2	9	7	3	8			1	7
2	1	9			8	4		1	4	9	2	8
		1	7	9	3				1	2	3	4
9	6		1	8		9	8	1	2			
8	2			1	9	8	7	4	5	2		
2	1	9			8	1	2			9	2	1
		2	9	3	6	5	4	1			8	2
		7	1	4	2		8	1			9	6
5	9	7	8				1	9	3	4		
3	8	1	4	2		2	9			9	1	2
2	7			9	7	3	6	2	1	8	4	5
1	6			7	2			9	5		2	9

PUZZLE 98

1	9	5				2	6	7	8	1	9	
6	7	9	1	8		4	5	6	7	2	8	9
	6	7	4	9	8		1	3	9		6	1
9	2	4			7	1	3	2	4		7	8
4	1	3			9	5			1	9	2	3
		6	2			9	8	1		4	3	
		8	4	1	7	3	5	2	9	6		
	9	2		4	9	8			7	3		
9	6	1	8			4	8			2	5	6
2	3		6	7	8	2	9			5	9	4
8	5		1	8	9		7	3	5	1	2	
1	2	6	3	4	5	8		8	9	7	6	4
	1	8	2	3	4	9			8	7	2	

PUZZLE 99

1	8			9	2	4		8	7		9	8
4	9	8		5	3	7	8	9	6		7	9
	1	9	8	3			4	2	1		6	5
		6	4	1	2				9	6	2	1
5	9	1		6	7	2	1	3		9	3	
2	7		9	7		8	6	9	2	7	1	
	2	8	1		8	6	2		9	8	4	
	3	9	7	4	2	1		8	1		8	7
	1	7		8	9	5	1	4		8	5	1
2	4	5	1				4	7	2	1		
8	6		9	8	6			9	8	2	1	
9	8		5	2	1	4	7	3		9	3	1
6	5		2	1		7	8	5			6	7

PUZZLE 100

9	6		2	1			5	1		8	1	
5	4	8	9	7		3	4	2	1	9	8	7
	2	1			1	4		8	3		5	1
1	5	3	2	4	7	9	6		7	1		
7	9		6	5			9	3		2	8	
2	7		3	2	8	9		2	3	8	9	
4	8		1	3	2	4	9	6	8		3	1
	1	8	9	6		1	7	4	6		4	2
	3	9		1	3			5	1		5	4
		1	4		4	5	6	1	2	3	7	8
2	8		7	1		1	7			4	6	
3	6	5	9	7	1	2		8	9	1	2	3
	9	3		9	4			1	5		1	6

PUZZLE 101

8	9	7			1	5			4	8	9	
1	8	3	7	9		4	3	9	8	6	5	7
	6	1	3	7				8	3	1	2	
9	3			1	9	5	4	2		3	9	
3	1	5	2		8	2	1			2	6	8
8	2	9	7	6	3	1		9	2		7	3
			9	8	6	7	5	2	1			
6	1		8	1		9	8	4	3	1	6	2
9	5	3			9	4	2		8	6	9	7
	9	4		9	4	3	1	8			2	1
	7	6	9	3			2	8	9	5		
9	3	2	5	1	8	7		1	2	8	3	9
8	2	1			9	1			7	1	6	

PUZZLE 102

4	2	9	1	8			3	9			6	1
6	7	5	2	9	8		1	5	7	9	8	4
8	1		3	6	9	8	7		3	6		
		9	7		1	9		9	5	7	8	
	4	5		9	2	1		6	1	8	5	
9	8		1	7		4	9	2			3	9
2	3		5	8	9	2	3	1	4		6	5
7	6			4	1	5		4	9		1	8
	7	2	4	1		3	1	8		2	7	
	9	7	8	5		6	2		4	8		
	1	6		4	7	3	1	5		6	2	
4	1	8	9	3	2		4	2	1	9	8	6
9	6			9	8			4	2	1	9	3

	1	3			3	8		8	2	1		
	8	9	6	3		7	9	8	5	3	2	1
8	9	4	3	1	7		1	7		9	8	3
1	5			5	8			1	3		9	2
		1	4	2			1	3	4	9		
	8	7	9			1	6	2	5	3	9	4
9	2		1	2	3	6	8	9	7		8	1
5	1	3	7	4	8	9			1	4	2	
		2	5	1	9			1	2	8		
3	8		8	7			1	7			2	7
9	7	8		8	1		8	9	2	1	4	3
1	4	5	8	9	7	3		8	5	7	9	
	6	9	7		9	6			2	3		

2	7	9		8	5		2	8	9		1	7
1	6	8	9	7	4		1	3	6	7	8	9
3	8		3	2	1	6	8	9		1	9	
4	9		8	4	2	9		6	4			
		9	2	1			1	5	8	3	4	
7	9	3				9	4	7		5	2	4
2	8			1	8	3	2	4			8	1
1	6	9		2	6	1				1	9	8
	2	4	1	7	9			1	3	6		
		6	9		1	4	2	8			1	8
	6	8		4	1	7	2	6	9		2	5
2	1	4	7	8	9		1	3	2	4	9	7
6	7		1	3	7		8	4		6	8	9

1	7		7	2			1	2			5	1
3	8		8	5	2	1	9	7		1	9	8
	3	2	1		9	3			1	3		
8	9	7	2	1		9	5		7	9	1	
3	2	1		9	2		9	7	2		9	4
4	1		9	7	8	6	3	1		9	3	1
		2	3		7	9	1		2	5		
8	9	3		7	9	8	2	3	5		5	1
1	5		9	6	5		4	9		1	6	8
	1	9	7		1	6		1	2	6	8	9
	5	1		9	1		1	7	9			
9	7	1		8	9	5	4	3	7		2	3
5	2			1	8			4	5		7	5

8	3			9	8	3		4	8		6	7
3	2	1		6	2	1		8	1	6	2	5
9	4	2	5			7	1			7	5	
2	1		4	7	9		9	3			4	3
	9	2	1	6	8		1	2	3	8	9	
8	9	7	1		3	9		2	7	8	9	
1	5		8	1	2	6	9			3	9	
	8	9	7	2		4	9		8	5	1	2
9	7	5	2	1		1	3	5	9	4		
6	3			3	9		1	2	7		8	1
	6	9			5	3			4	1	5	2
6	1	7	5	4		8	1	2		7	9	8
7	4			7	6		9	5	8		7	3

	6	9		1	3	9			4	9	5	8
2	3	4	1	6	8	7	9		1	2	3	7
1	8			7	9		4	9			1	2
8	9			8	2	1		3	2	1	4	9
		9	6		9	4			9	2	6	
	9	7	5			8	9	3		3	7	
	7	3		4	9	7	2	1		4	8	
	8	4		1	2	6			2	8	9	
	6	1	9			5	1		8	9		
8	5	2	3	1		9	6	5			9	5
1	2			7	1			6	2		4	3
9	4	3	8		8	7	2	9	4	3	6	1
6	3	1	2			3	1	8			9	5

	1	7	8			2	1	7			4	9
	2	5	1	6	3	7	9	8	4		3	2
2	7			9	7			6	8	5	1	
1	9	7	8			5	9			9	2	
		1	6			3	4	9	8		7	3
9	7				2	1		3	1	9	6	8
2	6	9			9	2	4			7	9	6
1	4	5	9	8		4	8				5	1
3	8		4	1	8	9			2	7		
	2	9			1	7			7	9	1	4
	1	8	5	9			6	1			2	9
8	5		3	1	2	6	9	8	4	5	7	
2	3			3	7	9			1	8	9	

PUZZLE 109

PUZZLE 110

PUZZLE 111

PUZZLE 112

PUZZLE 113

PUZZLE 114

PUZZLE 115

PUZZLE 116

PUZZLE 117

PUZZLE 118

PUZZLE 119

PUZZLE 120

Number Fun for Everyone

Official's Kakuro Puzzles: The Latest Puzzle Craze

Attention all Sudoku fans; if you like Sudoku, you'll love Kakuro. This number puzzle is based on logical thinking like Sudoku, and will keep your brain sharp! It's perfect for all members of the family.

Official's Sudoku Puzzles: The Puzzle Everyone's Solving

Offering the best in Sudoku puzzles, ranging from easy to brain-busting, you'll have fun with each and every one.

ANOTHER FINE KAPPA PUBLICATION